The Space Dealers

THE SPACE

THE JOHN DAY COMPANY · NEW YORK

DEALERS

A Hard Look at the Role of American Business
in Our Space Effort

EDWIN P. HOYT

The John Day Company, 257 Park Avenue South, New York, N. Y. 10010 an Intext *publisher*

Published on the same day in Canada by Longman Canada Limited.

Library of Congress Catalogue Card Number: 70-107204
Printed in the United States of America
Designed by The Etheredges

Contents

Acknowledgments

The author is indebted to a large number of people for information that went into this book. More or less in the order of their interviews, they are: Walter A. Pennino, deputy director of public information, NASA; Ralph Gibson, news chief, NASA; William Putnam, once Apollo program historian, later an employee of RAND Corporation; Eugene M. Emme, NASA historian, and Lee Siegesser, NASA historical archivist; Boyd C. Myers, deputy assistant administrator; Ralph E. Cushman, special assistant in the Office of Administration; George Vecchietti, director of procurement, NASA;

Paul A. Barron, deputy director; John H. Koepf, industry assistance officer; Jacob M. Roey, small business advisor; Harvey M. Kennedy, Jr., assistant director of procurement for administration; Dr. Frank D. Hansing, director, Sustaining University Program, NASA; Martin Sacks, special assistant to Bernard Moritz in the Office of Special Contracts, Negotiation, and Review; Pitt G. Thome, advanced programs director, Office of Space Science and Applications; Michael L. Garbacz, TIROS program manager; Paul E. Cotton, programs and resources division director, Office of Advanced Research and Technology, NASA; William O'Donnell, Apollo information division; John Kley, NASA information; W. E. Van Dyke, North American-Rockwell Corporation; Henry Siegal, Fairchild-Hiller Corporation; John Corson, the Urban Coalition, once of McKinsey & Company; John D. Young, Bureau of the Budget; Daniel Arons, Office of the General Counsel, NASA; Edward Redding, NASA Office of University Affairs; James E. Webb, former administrator of NASA; Herbert I. Butler, director of operational satellites, Goddard Space Flight Center; Howard W. Fensterstock, general counsel, The Renegotiation Board; P. E. Wagner and C. E. Dynes, both of American Telephone and Telegraph Company; Ted Hechler, NASA Manned Space Flight program; Charles F. Ducander and Denis C. Quigley, staff of the U.S. House of Representatives Committee on Science and Astronautics; James Gehrig, staff of the Senate Committee on Aeronautical and Space Sciences; Herbert Roback, staff administrator, House Military Operations Subcommittee of the Committee on Government Operations; Burt English, Aerospace Industries Association; William McBride, Martin Marietta Company. Also the author owes debts to many persons at the Cape

Kennedy Space Center, to industry representatives at Cocoa Beach, and to countless secretaries, receptionists, and administrative assistants who provided information about various aspects of the space business.

The Space Dealers

The Space Business

In 1971 the aerospace industry lies under an overcast of economic recession that threatens to obscure the major public issue of the industry—a growing concentration of power in an ever smaller number of hands. Because of the recession, few people wanted to consider the problems of concentrated economic activity—when thousands of capable and highly trained specialists were out of jobs. Hardly the time for cavilling, it would seem. And on the surface it would appear that the problem of the aerospace industry was too little attention by government that had turned elsewhere.

But as in the half-forgotten past, all it would take to arouse a new furore of activity in space would be some major development, probably one carried out by the Russians. In the meantime the real anguish of the specialists and their families who had been turned out by the industry tended to obscure the continued and even growing dangers of concentrated economic power in this aerospace industry. And indeed the successful, unspectacular moon landings without men carried out by the Soviets in the last months of 1970 lent emphasis to the whole questioning of America's space policy, even if in a different way. Many American scientists had long said that unmanned space flights, while not so glamorous, were equally valuable, far less expensive, and scientifically more easily viable than the manned variety. That is speaking theoretically. Speaking technically, we have developed so many space specialists in recent years, and the field is so narrow and circumscribed, that when an aerospace company fails or cuts its work force substantially, there are serious economic reverberations, and, equally vital, an important loss in momentum that may not easily be regained.

Quite aside from the recession of 1970–71 the space business finds itself in trouble that can affect the whole American economy. The point is that not merely "space industry" but the entire aerospace industry is involved. Thus the troubles are widespread, and they become more so as the number of dollars spent continues high but the number of companies spending them grows smaller. To blunt criticism, aerospace industrialists talk about subcontracts and the number of workers employed. But in fact it is virtually impossible now for a new company to arise and compete successfully as a prime contractor in aerospace. As they say in the trade, the ante has gotten just too big for that.

The trouble with the space industry, unlike the oil or garment industries, is that it burgeoned all at once in World War II, and ever since then events have outstripped planning. Only now, with the decision of the Nixon Administration to control space events, has there been an attempt at serious planning. But no single nation's plan can remain long in effect unless international planning soon follows. The first Sputnik and the public American hysteria that accompanied it demonstrated that no American administration could afford to "let the Russians get ahead." President Nixon has some control of space today only as a result of President Kennedy's huge space push in 1961 which put the Americans ahead of the Russians for a moment and brought us our present breathing space. But the confusion that still exists in a complex industry is manifest in the resignations of many scientists; the politically risky business of bringing Wernher von Braun, the former rocket expert for Nazi Germany, to Washington in a sensitive political post in the National Aeronautics and Space Administration; and the duality of the space effort (manned and unmanned). Some questions have been settled: for example, when American Telephone and Telegraph tried to secure a monopoly of the industrial space business it was slapped down by President Kennedy and an international organization was formed. But that organization is not functioning well, and unless something concrete is done in the next few years, countries smaller than the United States will be wasting money on space (they are already) and cluttering up space with vehicles and other hardware that cannot be of much use to mankind but will create waste and navigational problems for the future.

All the way through, the American space business has been notable for: its rivalries and differences of opinion, some of them very costly to the country and to science in general; the struggle of the existing aeronautical companies to dominate the field; the dichotomy between government advance and private industrial control; and the military-industrial idea that given enough money, given enough willingness to spend and duplicate and make mistakes, the country (and American business) can accomplish anything.

Sometimes there are costly mistakes, like the C-5A, which has turned out to be the greatest white elephant in American military history. Sometimes there are triumphs, such as little Explorer I, the satellite that outlasted everyone's hopes for it. The net is a picture typical of our times: that of an American effort burdened by all the evils that beset huge bureaucracy, enlivened by the competitive nature of the country even with government's big hand in the background, and given hope by visionaries who see beyond the immediate problems and pettinesses.

To understand the space business requires a knowledge of its history, its growth from the aviation industry at the end of World War II. One must realize that long before that war some kind of rocket research was going on in every country in the world—but no one in power was paying much attention. (To understand how Wernher von Braun is where he is, one needs to examine what happened in Germany in the 1930's.) And a study in contrasts is valuable: how the Russians followed one route and the Western world another, or rather, how various countries followed their own routes to begin the studies that would some day launch men in a rocket bound safely for the moon.

The most important development in bringing the military value of the rocket to public attention began in Germany in the 1920's. This work culminated there in the Me 262, a jet fighter plane which was envisaged by the rocket experts of Germany in 1938 and solved as an engineering problem in 1943. Only the stupidity of Hitler and his top planners prevented the Germans from building and using enough Me 262's early in the war to truly affect the outcome.[1]

The dual successes of the German effort to put artillery and vehicular propulsion into practical use before anyone else resulted in part, at least, from cooperation among a variety of manufacturers. The German military, of course, put up most of the money. But in the airplane field, particularly, several German airplane and engine manufacturers worked on the practical engineering. The Messerschmitt plane was powered by a Junkers engine. The Heinkel Company had worked on jets. So had the Bavarian Motor Works, while Rheinmetall-Borsig in Berlin and Schmidding und Dynamit in Bodenbach put their efforts into the chemistry of fuels. Meanwhile, they all had the cooperation of Theodore von Karman, Wernher von Braun, and the other German rocket experts.[2]

In the United States the story was quite different. Dr. Robert Hutchins Goddard began experimenting with rockets before World War I. In 1919 he wrote a small pamphlet called "A Method of Reaching Extreme Altitudes," which was published by the Smithsonian Institution and represented at that moment the most advanced thinking in rocketry. But while Opel and other manufacturers in

[1] Walter R. Dornberger, "The German V-2," in *The History of Rocket Technology*, edited by Eugene M. Emme, Detroit, Wayne State University Press, 1964, pp. 43–45.
[2] Wernher von Braun and Frederick I. Ordway III, *History of Rocketry and Space Travel*, New York, T. Y. Crowell Co., 1966, Ch. 4.

Germany were interesting themselves in the practical applications of rocketry, Goddard was constantly hampered by lack of funds, and what he did get came largely from the Smithsonian Institution and the Guggenheim family, which had established a foundation to encourage aeronautical development.

Around the world, there were many others working on rockets. The Russian Konstantin Ziolkovsky was probably the first. Edward Pendray and other members of the American Rocket Society were among the leaders. Hermann Oberth in Germany produced a pamphlet that became the basis for space travel philosophy. Robert Esnault-Pelterie studied astronautics in France with much success. But Esnault-Pelterie's work was financed partly by himself, partly by a banker friend. Oberth paid most of the printing bill for his historical pamphlet out of his ragged pocket. Goddard became so obsessed with financial problems and patents that he withdrew from the cooperative society of scientists. Later, as these experts continued their work, they were financed partly by their governments. But Goddard, for example, never reaped the financial rewards of his work until after his death, when the federal government finally awarded a million dollars to his estate on the basis that practically no rocket work could be carried out in America without violating Goddard's patents.[3]

In Britain, a young cadet at the Royal Air Force college named Frank Whittle wrote a thesis on jet propulsion and gas turbine engines in 1928. He was possessed of a sufficiently commercial mind to begin filing patents on his inventions two years later. He and others formed a company

[3] Milton Lehman, *This High Man, the Life of Robert H. Goddard*, New York, Farrar Straus and Co., 1963, p. 404.

called Power Jets Ltd., and on May 15, 1941, a jet plane was flown in England (Gloster 28/39) powered by a Whittle W-1 engine. By this time Britain was heavily dependent on American production for war weapons, and commercial considerations were sacrificed. In July 1941, the British disclosed their jet thinking to the United States Army Air Force, and the Bell Aircraft Company and General Electric began working on the Whittle-Gloster ideas. On October 1, 1942, the Bell XP-59A was successfully flown, and America had a jet aircraft, while in England the Rolls-Royce and Rover companies were working on jet engines under government contract, along with Metropolitan-Vickers.[4]

The Russians, working all by themselves, were nearly up to the Germans in pure and practical scientific advances in jet propulsion and rocketry by this time, and ahead of the Western allies. But the Russians had special problems of production, caused partially by their system of government ownership and partially by the exigencies of war.

The first experimental Soviet jet-fighter was designed by V. F. Bolkhovitinov, in 1939 and 1940, and tested in 1941. But production was difficult because the main industrial centers of the USSR had been occupied by the Germans or moved to the eastern section of the country. Russia's problem was to survive, and to obtain weapons where it could. Further, said one of Russia's leading rocket scientists much, much later, "as admitted by the XXth Congress of the Communist Party itself, Stalin and his lieutenants had committed too many mistakes in preparing the country's defenses."[5]

[4] J. L. Nayler, and E. Ower, *Aviation: Its Technical Development*, Philadelphia, Dufour, 1965, Ch. XII.
[5] G. A. Tokaty, "Soviet Rocket Technology," in *The History of Rocket Technology*, p. 278.

There is a study in contrasts. In the two countries where rocket technology was probably most advanced, the military dictators were not sufficiently impressed in time to bring that technology to fruition for the great war. In America and England, where the governments had been totally unimpressed with rocketry prior to the war years, private industry, combined with government, began to make long strides very quickly.

One of the most interesting studies in such contrast is the formation of the Aerojet-General Corporation, which came almost solely from scientific development and the economic development of scientists. The Corporation had its beginnings in the 1930's at the Guggenheim Aeronautical Laboratory of the California Institute of Technology, where Theodore von Karman had come to study and teach aerodynamics and subjects related to rocketry. In 1936 this laboratory began building rockets. Frank Malina, a staff member, visited Goddard in Roswell, New Mexico, where the pioneer rocketeer had gone to make his home, to secure rocket information, but Goddard was suspicious and withdrawn by that time.

Around 1938 the first American business firm took an interest in the rocket work of the laboratory. Consolidated Aircraft Company of San Diego was working on jet-assisted take-off problems for the aircraft industry; its company president solicited a report on the subject from Malina, to be included in a talk before the National Academy of Science's Committee on Army Air Corps Research in Washington. Out of this came an offer from the Academy to support the laboratory's research with a grant of $1,000.

In 1939 the Academy gave Cal Tech $10,000 for Jet-Assisted Take-off (JATO) research. A year later there was progress to report, and soon the first JATO rockets were built. These were the direct ancestors of the large solid-propellant engines developed much later. On the basis of the reported progress, Major Benjamin Chidlaw persuaded the Air Corps to spend its own money on the Cal Tech project, and on August 12, 1941, the first successful tests of JATO were made.

The jet engine was now proved, by Whittle in England and the Cal Tech people in America. Malina began thinking about the commercial possibilities. He was encouraged in these thoughts by John W. Parsons, a self-trained chemist who had joined the rocket program along with Edward S. Forman, a skilled mechanic.

In 1941, they began talking about incorporation. They could see a need for the development of both solid and liquid fuel engines for the Air Force and other armed services. They were thinking not entirely as scientists, but also as businessmen: why shouldn't they share in the profits to be made from the exploitation of the ideas they had developed over the years at Cal Tech? In the fall of 1941 they approached von Karman and found that he agreed. In the spring of 1942 the Aerojet General Corporation was formed, with von Karman as president and the others as officers.

Soon Aerojet had a quarter-million-dollar Air Force contract. The company secured the backing of the Defense Plant Corporation and $149,000 for construction of a plant. It bought land near Azusa, California, at $350 an acre—land that twenty-five years later would be worth $25,000 an acre, by von Karman's calculation. The company, of course, could not claim omniscience any more than the aircraft industry. Aerojet's tiny beginnings were simply a wave of the future; Northrop Aircraft, Hughes Aircraft, and Air Research Corporation had not had the foresight to pick up the company when it was offered. Who would know that in a score of years Aerojet would be a three-quarter-billion-dollar business with a force of thirty-four thousand employees?[6]

By 1943 the jet engine had been accepted in the United States. That year Lockheed Aircraft Company was given a contract by the Army air forces to engineer and build a jet fighter (the P-80, or Shooting Star). But the point was, it had to be done fast.

Lockheed had a tried and true system of engineering and construction, but this would not do for the rush job. So Lockheed executives sat down to figure out a way to do it. The outcome was the establishment of an entirely separate group in the company's engineering department for development of this airplane. H. L. Hibbard, vice president and chief engineer, was in charge. Under him and responsible for the project was C. L. Johnson, chief research engineer. Johnson had four assistants; under them were 130 engineers, draftsmen, and artisans. The air force at Wright Field gave them 180 days to do the job.

It took thirty-five days to assemble the crew in an eleven thousand-square-foot temporary building next to the company wind tunnel. But in nineteen days they had a wooden mockup of the plane. (The jet engine would be supplied by the British, who were further advanced in this field.) The engineers had to work out a new airfoil for a wing. The staff worked a ten-hour day six days a week, and did the job—then discovered that this rush system had cost the company only 63 per cent of what it cost to build the prototype of the XP-38, Lockheed's conventional twin-engined fighter.

6 Theodore von Karman with Lee Edson, *The Wind and Beyond*, Boston, Little, Brown and Co., 1967, Ch. 32.

And so the stage was set. In 1944 General H. H. Arnold gathered together a group of scientists to plan research for the years ahead. Theodore von Karman was deeply involved in this project. In the beginning, he encountered considerable difficulty in hiring men from industry because—how far we have come!—the military officials did not trust the industrial firms to give them disinterested advice.[7]

Shortly before the end of the war, Dr. von Karman led a team of scientists into Germany to check on German rocket developments. Peenemunde, on the Baltic coast, was in the hands of the Russians, but the group discovered a secret institution near Braunschweig in northern Germany that had important material such as a study of the swept-back wing and delta for supersonic flight—concepts that quite changed the work of Boeing in Seattle, where engineers were working on a transonic bomber plan. Immediately, obviously, the experimental work of the Germans had implications for American industry.[8]

Also before the war ended, von Karman and his friends had a lesson in business practice. Two years after Aerojet was set up, the company found itself in a difficulty not unusual for small businesses in America: under capitalization. President Andrew Haley approached the General Tire and Rubber Company of Akron, Ohio. Negotiations began, and Aerojet turned down an offer of backing in favor of a buyout of stock. The Aerojet owners wanted $225,000 for half the stock. In January 1945 they actually got $75,000. By 1953 the financial maneuverings had exhausted von Karman, who sold out. Ten years later he calculated that the sale cost him $12 million.[9] At about this time nearly all the

[7] Von Karman, p. 269.
[8] *Ibid.*, p. 277.
[9] *Ibid.*, p. 319.

original group who had founded Aerojet were out of the company, sadder but wiser men.

Several aspects of rocketry were beyond the resources of private companies during the developmental period of the 1940's, even had the aircraft industry engaged in aggressive planning for the future. Basic propulsion of the big rockets was of primary concern.

The first step toward this in America was taken by the Jet Propulsion Laboratory at Cal Tech for the Army ordinance department. The studies began in 1944 when it became apparent that the Germans were on to something very important at Peenemunde. When von Karman went to Washington to help create the scientific advisory board for the Air Force, Frank Malina took over leadership of the Jet Propulsion Laboratory work. This JPL, as it was called in the trade, became America's first center for space research and long-range missiles. By war's end it had thirty-two acres in the Arroyo Seco area of Pasadena and a three-million-dollar plant. The laboratory began building rockets, starting with Private A, the first American missile propelled by a long-range solid propellant engine. It flew 11 miles in tests at the end of 1944. By 1945, tests were being conducted at the White Sands Proving Grounds on the Wac Corporal, a 16-foot rocket that weighed 665 pounds. The engine had been built by Aerojet. The vehicle assembly had been done by Douglas Aircraft. On October 11, the rocket set a new altitude record of 235,000 feet, and after this performance the people at JPL began talking space flight with such confidence that even industry became interested. The method would be piggyback—the staging of rockets—and it was estimated at this time that the V-2 and Wac Corporal together could put the Wac up to a point 375 miles above earth. (The experiments were tried, and in February 1949 the Wac Corporal ascended to 244 miles above earth, to become the first man-made object thrown into outer space.)

At the end of the war, not too many Americans had faith in the big rockets. Dr. Vannevar Bush told the Special Senate Committee on Atomic Energy in December 1945 that he believed the intercontinental ballistic missile was not going to be feasible for a very long time. He was giving a very general opinion, although various elements in the Army, Navy, Air Force, and industry were working on just such problems. The Navy Bureau of Aeronautics began in October 1945 to study space rocketry, and in December placed a contract with the Guggenheim laboratory at Cal Tech. But the Navy did not have the five million dollars that was necessary, and in the postwar atmosphere of released tensions, it was very unlikely that the Navy or anyone else was going to get it.[10]

The Navy and the Air Force got together enough to meet and discuss mutual problems and areas of interest in the joint earth satellite program. But the meetings, held in 1946, bogged down in interservice rivalry. In 1945 the Air Force established project RAND, which was to investigate the space-flight problem. Project RAND was operated by the Douglas Aircraft Corporation, with interest and some participation by North American Aviation and Northrop. The RAND people foresaw the feasibility of a world-circling spaceship that could be put into orbit by staging rockets. But these scientists could not figure out any useful reason for the flight. What could be done with the satel-

---

[10] R. Cargill Hall, "Early U.S. Satellite Proposals," a paper originally written for a National Space Club competition, reprinted in *History of Rocket Technology*, pp. 67–71.

lite? The ballistic missile was not considered because it hadn't enough power to lift the heavy weight of an atomic bomb. In the end, because no weapons use could be found for the project, it was suspended.

More studies were made, but the huge amounts of money necessary to make tests were not forthcoming. At this time rocketry, the practical application of twentieth-century space science, fell into three provinces: those of the Army, the Navy, and the Air Force. As von Braun and Ordway put it: "Because of continuing interservice rivalry, the Army, Navy, and Air Force for many years carried on what were essentially separate missile development programs that made contact with each other only occasionally. Not until the mid-1950's did the Defense Department come to grips with the problems caused by the three services' differing outlooks and stubborn independence."[11]

One might say, then, that during this period the space business was spread out all over the lot.

All the company heads had to do was look at the record of the aircraft companies that were developed during the First World War. Four major companies built three-quarters of the airplanes and engines used by the services. They were Curtiss Aeroplane and Motor Corporation, Standard Aircraft Company, Wright-Martin Company, and Dayton-Wright Company. Not one of the four firms survived the war letdown without reorganization; Standard Aircraft went out of business altogether; and Dayton-Wright went out of the airplane business. Small companies tended to disappear without a trace, as sales plummeted. Curtiss, as one of many, dropped in sales from $46 million in 1918 to $1.3 million in 1921.[12]

[11] Von Braun and Ordway, p. 120.
[12] *Ibid.*, p. 37.

As the war drew to an end, and concurrently the military increased its interest in jet propulsion and the attendant problems of supersonic and space flight, some important options began to appear. Should the companies concentrate on current production and current thinking? In 1944 three companies—Goodyear, Vought, and Brewster—were producing the F4U fighter for the Navy. As the fighter was replaced by more advanced planes, the Brewster contract was canceled. Brewster, then, had that kind of decision to make. In a way, the busiest companies in these last months of the war were in the most danger. Unless they had already opted to pursue the space business.

One busy little firm was Reaction Motors, Inc., a firm formed in 1942 by several members of the American Rocket Society for basically the same reasons that von Karman and his associates formed Aerojet. Reaction Motors was eagerly seeking government contracts to build jet engines. (Later Reaction Motors was absorbed by Thiakol Chemical Corporation.)

But more practically, other existing aircraft firms began to drift into the transonic or supersonic business. Bell Aircraft was just about the first of them. In 1941 General Arnold secured a Whittle jet engine from England, and it was turned over to General Electric Corporation for production of a jet engine of its own. Bell was given the job of building the airplane. When it was finished in 1942 and flown, this P-59 Airacomet, as it was called, managed to attain a speed of only slightly more than four hundred miles an hour. This speed was not much higher than that of conventional airplanes, and the jet's fuel consumption was too great to make it useful as a combat plane. But the work was begun and, as noted, Lockheed also was soon laboring on jet airframes.

Research and development were certainly possible if the government would foot the bill. In February 1945, Bell Aircraft was given the contract to build three transonic flight research planes that would be driven by liquid-rocket engines. This was the X-1 project. The engine would be built by Reaction Motors.

The Navy, at the same time, undertook a different project with Douglas Aircraft Company. The X-1 was to be a 1,700-mile-an-hour plane, reaching eighty thousand feet. (It never did make that speed.) The Navy, trying a turbojet rather than the direct-thrust principle of X-1, authorized experiment with the D-558-I, which was to take off and land by itself (the X-1 was to be dropped from a B-29).

The problems began to develop. The Bell people had a suitable airframe, but their rocket engine was not adequate for it. So the X-1 was tested out in gliding flight. By the summer of 1947, it had attained the speed of Mach 0.8, and in the fall X-1 surpassed the speed of sound. Bell continued to work on the airframe until the middle of the 1950's. In its experiments much was learned about structures and metals at high speed and low atmospheric density. Also, with these experiments the engineers began working on attitude control at very high altitudes, a matter that would be of specific interest in the manned space capsules that were to come later.[13]

In the early 1950's the Bell company was experimenting with new materials, including stainless steel and a nickel alloy called Monel K. Curtiss-Wright was working on an improved rocket power plant which was throttleable—that is, which could be controlled in the amount of thrust de-

[13] Kenneth Kleinnicht, "The Rocket Research Airplanes," in *The History of Rocket Technology*, p. 201.

livered, unlike previous engines. The X-2s were trouble-some, however, and two test pilots were killed in them.

In the 1950's NACA foresaw a need for research in flight at high altitudes (up to fifty miles) and at high speeds (up to Mach 10). By 1954, the government agency's engineers had conceived a project called the X-15. The Air Force would oversee design and construction by a private contractor. The Air Force and the Navy together would finance the program. The National Advisory Committee for Aeronautics would carry the responsibility for technical direction.[14]

NACA organized its Research Airplane Committee to oversee the job. Various aircraft firms were invited to discuss the problems and submit proposals or plans. In November 1955, North American Aviation was selected to build three supersonic airframes. Thus North American came in very much on the ground floor of the space business. Much had been learned in the flights of the early experimental vehicles; now it was proposed to build a plane that could fly at 6,600 feet per second and reach an altitude of 250,000 feet. A more radical departure was the proposed engine: Reaction Motors was employed to develop a 50,000-pound rocket engine which would deliver 500,000 horsepower at 4,000 miles per hour, twice as much, for example, as the engines of the supercarrier USS *Forrestal* at optimum operating power.[15]

For such a craft, entirely new concepts had to be engineered. Attitude-control devices had already been experimented with and now several small rocket engines to provide attitude control outside the normal atmosphere were planned. There were to be 1,100 sensors to record tempera-

14 *Ibid.*, p. 205.
15 *Ibid.*, p. 206.

tures, pressures, and stresses at various points. The Garrett Corporation's Airesearch manufacturing division was employed to provide environmental controls for the cockpit. The David Clark Company was to spend the next two and a half years making the XMC-2 pressure suit, which was air-conditioned and heat-reflective, with its own emergency oxygen and pressurizing system. This company edged into the space business; David Clark began as a brassiere manufacturer, got into war work making pressure cells for B-29 high-altitude bombers, and then built the space suit.[16]

So in the middle of the 1950's, work was well begun that would lend itself to the space business. Not all the people working on space problems believed that man could or would ever go into orbit—at least not in the twentieth century. Many of the doubters were in the aviation industry.

[16] Lloyd Mallan, *Men, Rockets and Space Rats,* New York, Julian Messner Inc., 1961.

2

The Uncoordinated Effort

There is a vast difference in the ways in which nations approach transcendental problems, those which require huge outlays of capital without hope of recompense in monetary terms for the sums laid out. If it was a matter of building a railroad across the country, private industry in a capitalist country could be counted on to do the job, and in a controlled state government would do it, with less efficiency and speed. But when it comes to something as immense as a national space program, there is a much greater difference in approach—and, in the case of a free economy, vast waste in uncoordinated effort.

In a laissez-faire economy like that of the United States, the need for centralized effort in military research is not easily seen. It takes a long time for the generals and admirals to accept a new idea—or it used to. During World War I, when the need for central planning was urgent, the beginnings of the space program were slow, small, and until 1917 hampered considerably by the skepticism of the military.

The history of the American space business, is bound up inextricably with that of the aviation business from which it sprang, and many of the practices of the space business stem from the beginning of aviation. Inventively speaking, the United States was very much a leader in the aviation business. In 1903 the Wright brothers developed basic principles of flight, such as aileron control, which have dominated the industry ever since. Yet a few years later, America was quite out of it, in terms of the development of the airplane for military and civilian use. The reason is that the aviation business in its first decade in America was left squarely in the hands of squabbling private industry, while in other countries governments took varying degrees of interest.[1]

The European war of 1914 pressed on American military and political leaders the need for a national aeronautical program. Within weeks after the beginning of hostilities in France, airplanes were being used as combat weapons, and it was apparent that their development would be fast and furious. The United States could not afford to be left out, so in 1915 the National Advisory Committee for Aeronautics (NACA) was established in Washington to coordinate development of aviation. The beginning was very small: Congress appropriated five thousand dollars for the com-

[1] Robert L. Rosholt, *An Administrative History of NASA, 1958–1963*, Washington, National Aeronautics and Space Administration, 1966, pp. 9–20.

mittee, a sum which permitted its members to meet occasionally, discuss research problems with industrial leaders and university professors, and carry on a limited correspondence. By 1920, however, the committee had a budget of $175,000, and on the edge of the Depression it had $1,508,-000 a year to spend, enough to permit a solid basic research program at the laboratory at Langley Field, Virginia. The program suffered during the Depression years, but in 1939 Congress authorized creation of a second laboratory (Ames Aeronautical Laboratory) at Moffett Field, California. Then, with a new war, the course was ever onward and upward.[2] A third laboratory was established at Cleveland's municipal airport, and in 1945 and 1947 two more facilities were added, at Wallops Island, Virginia, and Edwards Air Force Base in Southern California.

The national committee's major contribution to the space effort was probably the development of the X craft. These, designed for transonic and supersonic flight, inaugurated the studies of the design problems of aircraft to carry human beings beyond new boundaries. Historian Robert Rosholt notes that the importance of the NACA efforts lay in the broad nature of the program. The committee, through intelligent management over a long period of time, had attracted competent young scientists and engineers; it had $300 million worth of excellent research facilities, its personnel were engaged in research projects of their own choosing in their own laboratories; and the committee was respected by the scientific community for its approach and its work.[3]

All this was fine—as far as it went. But the problem was

[2] *Ibid.*, pp. 20, 21.
[3] *Ibid.*, pp. 22, 23.

that the National Advisory Committee on Aeronautics was geared to a leisurely pace. It was primarily a scientific organization, not a promotional body, not a clearing house or an agency equipped to undertake a concerted program for national defense (ballistic missiles and rockets) or space research, with an object to achieving optimum results in minimum time. And why should it be different? At the end of World War II, the United States felt secure in its apparently unchallenged possession of the atomic bomb. As far as rocketry was concerned, the Americans and British had captured most of the Peenemunde group, including von Braun and many other German rocket experts. The military and Congress had the feeling that there was no particular hurry, no special pressure for the development of supra-atmospheric rockets.[4]

The scientific community was not at all sure that rocketry was on a sound foundation. Dr. Vannevar Bush, director of the Office for Scientific Research and Development, seriously questioned the concept of an intercontinental ballistic missile. No one, outside a rather narrow group of rocket enthusiasts, wanted to spend the time or money on something that seemed unlikely to be needed for years. And the aviation industry was looking forward in terms of supersonic flight and jet-powered aircraft, but it was as yet outside the purview of most of that industry to dream of the conquest of space.

The military men took the lead, and if their manner of doing so was wasteful—which it was—this was because each of the three basic defense services looked upon the problems of rockets in terms of its own military needs.

[4] Wernher von Braun and Frederick I. Ordway III, *History of Rocketry and Space Travel*, Chapters 5, 6.

The most advanced planning was that done by the RAND project for the Army air force and that begun even earlier by the Navy's Bureau of Aeronautics. Both dealt with satellite vehicles that could be shot into space beyond the pull of earth's gravity. In 1945 and 1946 Navy and Air Force scientists were seriously studying these possibilities on paper.[5]

The Navy made its contract with the Guggenheim Laboratory of the California Institute of Technology, and from its study came valuable basic information about the problems of orbit, fuel, rocket structure, and the relationship of payload to rocket. Aerojet Corporation was given a contract to build a device that would test the value of a specific impulse of liquid hydrogen and oxygen, the purpose being to see whether the machine could achieve the theoretical values that would put a satellite into orbit with a single-stage rocket.

All this was well enough. The Bureau of Aeronautics was spending about two million dollars on such work. But to assemble a flight test vehicle and a program would cost somewhere between five and ten million dollars, and the Navy did not have the money. There was no indication in the winters of 1945 and 1946 that it would get the money, either.

The Navy then approached the Army air force, to see if they might cooperate on space research. But after toying with the idea, the Army air force rejected it. Unfortunately, Navy and Air Force were jockeying for position, so the program did not get off the ground.[6]

---

[5] R. Cargill Hall, "Early U.S. Satellite Proposals," in *History of Rocket Technology*, pp. 67 *et seq.*
[6] *Ibid.*, p. 72.

The Air Force's project RAND continued, and in 1946 the scientists of the three participating aeronautical companies (Douglas, North American, and Northrop) predicted that a satellite could be put into orbit in five years if the effort were made. The engineers of North American Aviation knew, even then, that a satellite could be achieved by the multistaging of rockets. Practically speaking, however, the trouble with the satellite program as it was presented was that it had no direct military value. It must be remembered that the scientists and engineers were talking to military men. The RAND people talked of satellites for weather forecasting and other astronomical uses, for relay of communications. Yet to the military this seemed hardly enough: how could such programs be justified to a Congress that was concerned with cutting back on military expenditures? True, L. N. Ridenour, one of the RAND consultants, pointed out the brotherhood between a satellite vehicle and a rocket that could carry a warhead across continents, but his words fell on deaf ears. It would be more than ten years before they would be remembered as predictions of things to come. In 1946 the services agreed to pursue their satellite studies separately. The Navy had a small contract with North American Aviation, and a joint contract with the Glenn L. Martin Company of Baltimore and Aerojet to investigate practical fuel and vehicle performances. The Air Force continued with its RAND studies.

The question of who should have jurisdiction over what types of rockets brought up some problems, for this was the period when the services were being combined under the Department of Defense. Each service was struggling to retain all the power it had and to gain new powers in the new establishment. The Air Force, for example, was very much concerned with maintaining the strategic bombing service, and emphasized the development of long-range aircraft capable of delivering atomic weapons across the world. This emphasis and economies of government guided matters; so for a time the Navy and the Air Force continued minor researches, but the satellite program in the late 1940's could hardly be said to be more than a dream.[7]

In 1948 Secretary of Defense James Forrestal referred to the satellite program in his annual report, but it would be six years before the plan would get very far ahead. The 1948 report did bring an outcry from the Soviet press, and very well may have engendered a stronger effort in Russia to move in this field than might otherwise have been the case. That, however, is speculation; the plain fact is that the Western World vastly underestimated the accomplishments of Soviet space science and rocketry in these years. Had anyone warned that the Russians were forging ahead, few if any Western political and military leaders would have accepted the judgment.

After all, the Americans had picked up most of the highly skilled German rocket experts of Peenemunde, and the military planners felt they could move at their own pace. For this reason, primarily, the space business was carried on independently by the three military services, with some research by private business. The Air Force devoted its efforts to building a series of "flying bombs." Northrop Aircraft Company built the Snark, which was powered by a Pratt and Whitney turbojet engine, with assistance from a pair of jet boosters built by Aerojet. The Glenn L. Martin Company built the Matador missile. North American got a contract to develop the Navaho missile. None of these was

[7] *Ibid.*, p. 83.

the intercontinental ballistic missile about which so much talk was circulating in the 1940's and early 1950's. Navaho was the valuable one, for through it North American's engineers (and others) learned a great deal about the technology of rocketry, in particular about guidance systems.

The Army worked on ballistic missiles, using the Germans from Peenemunde. They came to America in 1945 and 1946 with their V-2 rockets, and began work. Soon the General Electric Company was brought into the program. This was not long before the firings began at Cape Canaveral, Florida, a site which was to become the symbol of the American space program. Tests were also conducted at the proving grounds at White Sands, New Mexico, and these led to the establishment of the missile program at the Redstone arsenal in Huntsville, Alabama, in 1950. Three years later, the program having been speeded up by the dangers made obvious when the Korean war broke out, a Redstone missile was fired successfully from Cape Canaveral. At about this same time American intelligence authorities discovered that the Russians were well along on production of an intercontinental ballistic missile. In 1955 the Eisenhower Administration made the decision to concentrate efforts, rather than let the experts duplicate each other's research and expenses. A committee headed by James R. Killian, Jr., recommended that the Navy and the Army should both support development of an intermediate-range missile. The National Security Council accepted the recommendation, and the joint Army-Navy ballistic missile committee set to work on the project. Thus was born the Jupiter missile. By 1956, using the principle of multiple stages of rockets, the scientists fired a Jupiter C to an altitude of 682 miles. From this program the American space effort developed relatively quickly.

Still, in 1956 one could scarcely say that there *was* a space program. The joint Army-Navy committee was abolished. The Navy put out its own study contract to Lockheed Aircraft, which recommended the building of the missile (now called Polaris) that can be fired from a submarine under water. This planning developed a whole new concept in submarine warfare, which led to the building of the Polaris submarine fleet. The Air Force was developing the Atlas intercontinental ballistic missile. The Army was sticking with the Jupiter.[8]

These were the rockets—the forces of propulsion that would or could send a man-made object out into space beyond the pull of earth's gravity. Equally important, and far less noticed by the general American community, was research into the human factors entailed in travel in space. This work had begun in the 1940's.

It was not well known, for example, that a half dozen of Germany's aeromedical scientists had been brought to Wright-Patterson Air Force Base in Ohio after the war to work with the Air Force School of Aviation Medicine. In the late 1940's many doctors were willing to swear by their reputations that man could not function in space—perhaps could not even survive there. But as early as 1948 the Air Force doctors were separating and finding some solutions for the "aeromedical" problems of space travel. So tenuous was the concept's hold on the public however, that when the Lovelace Foundation for Medical Research of Albuquerque conducted a symposium on man and space flight in 1951, it was called simply Physics and Medicine of the Upper Atmosphere, although the majority of the forty-four speakers were talking only about space.

8 Von Braun and Ordway, Chapter 6.

Weightlessness and g-factors were the most important matters studied. By 1952 one of the Germans, Fritz Haber of the Air Force School of Aviation Medicine, had drawn up plans for a sealed chamber to be used in space research. Two years later the Guardite Company of Chicago delivered the chamber, which consisted of a 100-cubic-foot cabin with air-conditioning and oxygen systems and even a system for distilling urine to the purity of drinking water. Volunteers began to work in this chamber, and the doctors began to learn how man reacted to conditions simulating those of space flight.[9]

This work proceeded along with the research by NACA and its contracting companies. In the summer of 1957 a committee of the Air Force Scientific Advisory Board met at the Rand Corporation's offices in Santa Monica and discussed space flights in manned vehicles to orbit the earth and even go to the moon. Avco Manufacturing Corporation made a preliminary study of the ballistic approach to manned space flight. But Avco did this study really as a favor for the Air Force, without compensation, because there just was not money available for what the scoffers called the "Buck Rogers" approach, even by the summer of 1957.[10] The Air Force Research and Development Command wanted $200,000 that summer to conduct its own studies on manned space flight, but it did not get the money.

This uncoordinated work was going on in the days just before Sputnik.

[9] Lloyd S. Swenson, Jr., James M. Grimwood, and Charles C. Alexander, *This New Ocean, A History of Project Mercury*, NASA, 1966, pp. 34–52.
[10] *Ibid.*, p. 70.

3

Hurray for Sputnik

On October 3, 1957, America was fat and complacent, the richest society in the world, basking in its affluence, certain that it controlled the destiny of mankind. A few hours later a little beep-beep-beep that could be heard on radio sets had changed the world. The Russians had just won the greatest propaganda victory in the twentieth century. They had sent a satellite into orbit around the earth and proved that the United States did not have a stranglehold on "scientific Know-how" or the industrial ability to conquer a new field. America looked very, very foolish.

What happened in America in October 1957, then, was panic, which was equally fatuous. For years Americans had regarded the Russians as somehow inferior, the Soviet political system as incapable of producing either true or applied science. We had a ready political answer: how can lies produce truth? America believed then that she was the wellspring of all truths. It took precisely the Sputnik jolt to awaken the United States to its own shortcomings. Nothing else had succeeded. Earlier, when the Russians exploded a hydrogen bomb, everybody but the scientists put a premium on the spy cases—on the original thefts of information. But the beeping of Sputnik in the skies could not be passed off so easily. For a time, of course, the jokesters said that the Russians simply had better Germans than we had— but that comment soon became tiresome. The initial shock was followed by urgent and sometimes hysterical public outcry and action in favor of beefing up the study of science in America.

Meanwhile, however, the American space picture was not nearly so bleak as it seemed to the public. For a number of years scientists all over the world had been planning an International Geophysical Year, to run from July 1, 1957, through December 31, 1958. In 1953 the American Rocket Society had suggested that the United States include among its contributions to the IGY the orbiting of a small earth satellite. The idea was made appealing to the Eisenhower Administration and adopted in 1955, with the Navy chosen to supervise Project Vanguard. The trouble was that not enough money was made available. As Dr. Robert Rosholt said subsequently, in his *Administrative History of NASA, 1958–1963*: "One very fundamental thing revealed by Project Vanguard was that a successful space program would have to be built on a foundation of well-formulated policy and planning, be effectively organized, be firmly supported with resources, and given high priorities."[1]

These priorities simply did not exist in October 1957. More woe was heaped upon American heads a month later, on November 5, when the Russians put Sputnik II into orbit. Sputnik I was a small satellite, of about two hundred pounds. Sputnik II weighed eleven hundred pounds and carried a dog into space. The American public was so seriously worried by this chain of events that President Eisenhower felt it necessary to make a major speech on November 7, assuring the nation (truthfully) that the American defenses against atomic attack were sound. He also reported what few positive results of the American space program he could: most importantly that the American efforts had produced a nose cone that could survive re-entry into the atmosphere without burning up. He announced the appointment of James R. Killian, Jr., to the new post of Special Assistant to the President for Science and Technology. He reported that a President's Scientific Advisory Committee had been created.[2]

The President's speech expressed the national worry. For the first time in the years since the emergence of the United States as the world's first atomic power, another nation had been "first" in the development of a new tool of the utmost importance in scientific and military life. But if the blow to American prestige was tremendous, the scientific community had seen it coming months before. The Russians had reported in the spring of 1957 that they had created the rockets and technology to put a satellite in orbit.

[1] Rosholt, p. 6.
[2] An Administrative History of NASA, p. 6.

In September they had broadcast the wavelengths on which the Sputnik's beep could be heard. That same month they distributed the information to the American press in Moscow. So the "surprise" was relative—the American people were surprised because no one had told them what was going to happen until the satellite was up.

The crisis became one of confidence. Congress and the public reacted in much the same way, demanding to know just what had and had not been done in America to match the Russian efforts. And there was no more talk about "Buck Rogers" equipment, particularly after Sputnik II went up bearing its dog.

The scientists worked along with the engineers. The politicians and press explored the public problems along with the politicians. Meanwhile at Cape Canaveral, the rocket engineers made ready to recoup with one or two launchings of America's own. One was the Vanguard. The other was the new Jupiter-C. Since such events are conducted publicly rather than in secret in the United States, the press made a great fiesta of the occasion. All the more was the American discomfiture, then, when on December 6, Vanguard ignominiously blew up on its launching pad instead of speeding into space. The American answer to the Russian challenge was a loud sizzling noise—a dud. It was, as rocket historian Willy Ley put it, "the most publicized failure in history." The reason for the failure was not really known. The General Electric Company, which had built the engine, blamed the Martin Company, which had built the vehicle, and Martin blamed GE. But the fact was that Vanguard had been rushed for more than scientific purposes. The second stage had never been tested in flight.[3] From

[3] Willy Ley, p. 318.

both an engineering and scientific point of view, such failure was completely understandable. From a public point of view it was inexplicable, and it brought feelings of frustration, anger, and even despair in the United States to new strengths.

From the depths of the gloom came positive results, however, what the authors of *This New Ocean* called "a remarkable alteration in practically everyone's thinking about space exploration."[4] At this time in American history, the most effective and active work in manned space flight was being done by Avco Manufacturing Company: late in November they submitted to the Air Force a plan to put a capsule on an Atlas missile, attaching a stainless steel cloth parachute to the capsule which would brake the capsule through the heat and speed of re-entry into the atmosphere. Avco had been spending some left-over government contract funds on its planning. Just before the end of 1957 the company asked for half a million dollars to make a three-month study and a full-scale model of the proposed vehicle. But there was too much confusion in the variegated space program at the moment, and the contract was never given out.

The decision to be made about the space business at this point was basically political. Unification of the three military services had not lessened their competition for anything each might be able to bring within its own orbit. The Air Force, feeling strongly that space belonged within its purview, moved first. Secretary of the Air Force James Douglas appointed a committee of fifty-six scientists and Air Force officers to propose a program. Edward N. Teller, the nuclear physicist, headed the committee. In time it came

4 *This New Ocean*, p. 71.

up with the germ of a long-range space program for the Air Force. The Air Force set up a Directorate of Astronautics—which lasted precisely three days before Secretary of Defense Neil McElroy decided the Air Force was trying to seize first place with a grandstand play. The Directorate of Astronautics disappeared from the table of organization.[5]

Very shortly the Air Force prepared a five-year plan for astronautics and communicated with the National Advisory Committee on Aeronautics, asking NACA director Hugh L. Dryden to cooperate with the Air Force. Now the complications increased—for within NACA were scientists, engineers, and administrators who believed the civilian agency ought to be the guiding factor in the American exploration of space. Administrator Dryden approved in principle of the cooperative effort but told the Air Force that NACA would pursue its own line of investigation into manned space flight.

The gamesmanship intensified. As NASA historians have indicated, those within NACA quickly realized that unless they seized the initiative they would be swallowed up as individuals by the agency that took the leadership, with NACA losing all its powers and capabilities. So NACA established its own committee on space, under H. Guyford Stever, a dean at the Massachusetts Institute of Technology.

One of the most effective of the NACA committee members was James Van Allen of the National Academy of Sciences. He proposed a scientifically (as opposed to militarily) oriented National Space Establishment to lead in space exploration. Meanwhile, as Congress argued and the press debated in print, the Department of Defense an-

[5] *Ibid.*, p. 73.

nounced that it wanted to create an Advanced Research Projects Agency. By the end of the year this program was finding support in the White House and elsewhere. But also by the end of the year, NACA was proposing to amalgamate the efforts of the Defense Department itself, the National Academy of Sciences, and the National Science Foundation. In other words, NACA wanted to bring under one roof everyone who might want to work in space research.[6]

Congressmen debated this very basic question from nearly every conceivable angle during November, December, and January of that winter, in a discussion so intense and variegated that NASA's historians did not even attempt to summarize it. Senator Lyndon B. Johnson's Preparedness Investigating Subcommittee of the Senate Committee on Armed Services called seventy witnesses on twenty different days in hearings that totaled 2,300 pages. Given an average word count of about five hundred words to the page of a Congressional hearing, making allowances for short replies, that would come to 1,150,000 words—and that was only one investigation.

By the first of the year things in Washington were in not much more coordinated a pattern than they had been the day after Sputnik I. Affairs took a better turn when the Jupiter-C launch of Explorer I—America's first satellite—was accomplished in January and washed out some of the shame Americans seemed generally to feel about their scientific and engineering community.

But what kind of program was there to be, and who was to run it?

Up on Capitol Hill all the vested interests had their Congressional representatives. Bills were thrust into the

[6] *An Administrative History of NASA*, p. 7 (note).

hoppers of both houses giving the space program or aspects of it to all conceivable agencies, including the Atomic Energy Commission (a bill introduced by Senator Clinton Anderson). So confusing did the interplay become that in February President Eisenhower asked Dr. Killian to draw up a unified program. He set to work, assisted by scientific and government advisors and pushed by everybody with a vested interest.

Meanwhile, the Air Force and NACA, which had the inside track on thinking completed and work done, called a meeting of industry representatives at Wright-Patterson Air Force Base. Representatives came from Northrop, North American Aviation, Avco, McDonnell Aircraft Corporation, and Republic Aviation Corporation to make presentations. In varying degrees all these companies had been studying the problems of manned space flight. The Air Force planned to spend a half-million dollars for a study of an environmental system that would let a man survive in space.[7] General Curtis LeMay, Air Force Vice Chief of Staff, asked the researchers to select a contractor to present a specific plan for a man-in-space program quickly. The Army and the Navy were doing much the same.

As the activity proliferated, the Administration became concerned with the competition among the military branches. Early in February President Eisenhower took steps to bring the space race into cohesion. Secretary McElroy created an Advanced Research Project Agency to manage all space programs in the Defense Department. To head the new program the Administration went off into private industry, and brought back Roy W. Johnson, a vice president of the General Electric Corporation.

[7] *This New Ocean*, p. 78.

Eisenhower did not like it, but for a time it appeared that the military had affairs under their control, with the Air Force in ascendance. The Air Force called a conference for March at which industry, military, and civilian government leaders would hear specific proposals for a man-in-space program, speaking in terms of thirty first-stage Thor rockets and twenty second-stage rockets to carry out the program. In other words, the military was getting down to practical cases.

But while this plan was forming, NACA was conducting planning meetings of scientists, engineers, and administrators at the Ames laboratory and elsewhere. And meanwhile, Dr. Killian consulted with his advisers and came up with a program to submit to President Eisenhower.

The approach suggested by Dr. Killian, and endorsed by the President's Advisory Committee on Government Organization, advocated civilian control. One reason given was that scientists, engineers, and technicians would be needed in number, and the program should produce important civilian gains in scientific knowledge and application. Another was that the military men just could not get along.

Killian suggested the rebuilding of the National Advisory Committee on Aeronautics to do the job because of NACA's history as an organization able to cooperate with the military, but one which all these years had retained its civilian characteristics which did not repel nonmilitary-oriented scientists.

So as the Department of Defense and NACA made their separate plans, much more wisely the Administration made its own, and the outcome was the Administration request for Dr. Killian's program. The National Aeronautical and Space Agency would be established—if Congress so voted—absorbing NACA and administered by a single individual assisted by an advisory board.

On the space planning level, NACA was already at work. In the January meetings at Wright-Patterson Air Force Base, the NACA scientists and engineers presented the results of two studies of manned space capsules. One described a triangular vehicle with a flat bottom. The other called for a ballistic capsule with a heat shield and high drag, in which the pilot lay prone (to cut the G-effect), with re-entry being brought about by reverse rocket thrust at the apogee of the orbit and ending in a parachute-supported landing. This plan was presented by Maxime A. Faget of the NACA staff.

At the same time, the contractors—the business firms— were presenting the results of the studies they had made with encouragement from the Air Force. Aeronatronics proposed a man in a sphere inside a cone-shaped capsule. Martin proposed a zero-lift vehicle with controlled flight. Lockheed suggested an angle cone with the pilot facing toward the rear. Convair talked of a manned space station. Avco offered the 1,500-pound sphere with its steel cloth parachute. Bell offered several brief proposals for spheres and boost-glide vehicles. North American stuck with its basic X-15 idea.

Most ingenious were two industry proposals: the Republic proposal for a vehicle known as the Ferri sled, a 4,000-pound triangular device with a two-foot-diameter tube running around the leading and trailing edge which was actually a fuel tank for a final-stage solid propellant series of rockets in the wing tips. It was rather aeronautical in concept, with the pilot to eject finally from the capsule and parachute to earth. The other industry proposal, made by McDonnell Aircraft, consisted of a ballistic missile of the general design proposed also by Faget, to be launched from a two-stage rocket.[8]

As Congress considered the Administration's drastic proposal to organize the space effort, the Air Force and several of its contractors were moving right ahead with their independent attempts. Roy Johnson apparently believed that the Air Force would have the responsibility for putting a man in space. And by March 18, NACA had accepted the concept advanced by Maxime Faget and his associates for the design of the space craft. It would be in general configuration the design that was to be used in the Mercury project.[9]

At this time Avco and Convair were still working closely with the Air Force. But the Air Force lost faith, particularly after Maxime Faget criticized the whole approach. Whizzing along, as the politicians talked, the Air Force let two three-month study contracts for $370,000 each to North American Aviation and General Electric. North American worked out details of a design for a space cabin and General Electric worked on the environmental controls. The Air Force was definitely in a hurry, on the obvious principle of getting there "fustest with the mostest" and moving the course of space investigation toward Air Force interests.

Theoretically all was under the aegis of the Advanced Research Projects Agency, but that agency, with little past and a scarcely visible future, was not particularly in control. It held conferences, but no one put much faith in them. It did hold up funds wanted by the Air Force to make contracts that would put the Air Force man-in-space program into action.[10]

[8] *Project Mercury, A Chronology*, NASA, 1963, p. 14.
[9] *Ibid.*, p. 18.
[10] *This New Ocean*, p. 93.

During the spring and summer the Air Force and NACA pursued their separate ways, making some progress toward what would be the final direction of the space program. The NACA engineers and scientists refined the shape of the capsule after many experiments. Faget discovered and developed the contour couch, which could enable a man to accept far more G-force than any previous mount. The Air Force carried on a joint program of furious engineering and scientific activity and propaganda. In meetings that began on July 24 they pulled out their big guns: if administrator Johnson would only give them the funds, they could rush ahead and put the United States into space with a manned capsule before the Russians got there. But appealing as the idea was to jingoists, director Johnson resisted it, for, as he told the Air Force men bluntly, President Eisenhower did not see any reason for the military to go into space.

In the summer of 1958 Congress passed the National Aeronautics and Space Act, accepting generally the ideas that the Administration wanted, although Congressional leaders considered the relationships between civilian scientific effort and national defense policy more important than the Administration had indicated. This emphasis showed in the final product, which regained creation of a civilian-military liaison committee. Also, the office of administrator of NASA was made more political than President Eisenhower probably wished it to be, political in the sense of being responsive to political change. Some had thought director Dryden of NACA would automatically become head of the new agency. Not so. He was made deputy administrator, while T. Keith Glennan, president of Case Institute of Technology of Cleveland, was made administrator.

Dryden's retention was obviously intended to assure the continuation of all that was good in NACA—the spirit of teamwork with other agencies, the forward-looking research and development, and the ability to get jobs done well and relatively quickly. But the superimposition of a more political figure would assure Congressional and public support. Glennan was a Republican of renown in the middle west. As a former member of the Atomic Energy Commission, his politico-scientific credentials were in order, but the primary problem of the space agency was seen as one of spending a great deal of money quickly and intelligently, in what had turned out suddenly to be the most sensitive area of American life.

4

NASA

It could be said that the major positive function of Roy
Johnson of General Electric was to save the government a
great deal of money in the first half of 1958, for this was
the time when Army, Air Force, and NACA were competing most vigorously to put man into space and manage other exploration of the universe outside earth's atmosphere.

In retrospect, it seems that Johnson was like the little
Dutch boy with his finger in the hole in the dike, or perhaps
more like the animated cartoon versions of the folktale,

which show the little boy running from one hole to another to try to plug them all up. Army and Air Force, particularly, had major programs on the brink of operability, and they were clamoring for the expenditure of many millions of dollars. Roy Johnson and his Advanced Research Projects Agency men went from meeting to meeting, cautioning the participants to keep their requests down until basic policy matters had been resolved. The Army proposed to orbit a man by summer, 1960, at a cost of $106.6 million. The Air Force was moving ahead with Man-In-Space-Soon-est—its own program. And then, on July 29, 1958, President Eisenhower signed the National Aeronautics and Space Act. The basic research into space would be done by the new organization, NASA, although the Department of Defense would maintain its activities in space relative to defense.[1]

The creation of NASA might have been a serious mistake, had not the military agencies taken the decision in relatively good grace and chosen to accept the spirit as well as the letter of the law. T. Keith Glennan had been in Washington, waiting. He and Dryden took over the new organization, absorbing eight thousand employees of NACA and its $100-million appropriation. Within a short time the framework of the new agency was laid out: it would take over the Vanguard project from the Navy, the Explorer project from the Army, and the Jet Propulsion Laboratory, which had been an Army contractor. It would assume various study contracts, including the North American Aviation contract for a rocket engine with a thrust of a million pounds. It would be given nearly $120 million by the Air Force in space activity appropriations allocated to defense.

[1] *This New Ocean*, pp. 79–98.

Actually, no specific directive was laid down as to the responsibility for manned flight into space, and this continued during part of the summer to be a serious problem, with Air Force, Navy, and Army competing. The Army ballistic missiles division proposed to use a modified Redstone missile to shoot a man into space along a suborbital trajectory. NASA deputy administrator Dryden characterized this plan as about as valuable as shooting a lady from a cannon.[2]

Avco was still working to get a manned satellite contract through the Air Force. The Navy was planning an orbital mission in a cylindrical vehicle with spherical ends that would become in mid-flight a delta wing glider. Convair, which then manufactured the Atlas missile, was teamed with the Goodyear Aircraft Corporation to study this matter.

Meanwhile, NASA was being organized, and late in August President Eisenhower gave the civilian agency the responsibility for the manned space flight mission. Roy Johnson's Advanced Research Projects Agency agreed to join with NASA in the effort. By this time a large number of civilian contracting agencies had become aware of the imminence of a growing space program; some, indeed, had been developing their capabilities steadily since World War II. What was needed was organization and specific planning.

The organization began with an ad hoc committee appointed within NACA. The conferees understood what they were getting into, that they were taking a comfortable and long-established little agency, with a minuscule budget, and suddenly thrusting it into public view. They realized that one of their principal problems would be procuring con-

2 *Ibid.*, pp. 97–98.

tracts and managing relations with the outside business community. Heretofore, NACA had had scarcely any contracts with the business world. The agency had done its own basic research, and when it needed some hardware, such as airplanes or engines, it had usually managed to get them from the Department of Defense.

The NACA men knew all this was to be changed. So they came up with a plan that called for a greatly expanded business affairs department, headed by a comptroller who would be directly responsible to the head of NASA. This was the main structural change, reflecting a new emphasis on relations with a business community that would inevitably become vital to the agency and the space program.[3]

When administrator Glennan took office, he was favorably impressed by the organizational plan of the interim committee, but he also recognized that some outside advice would be valuable. He turned to John Corson, then manager of the Washington office of the management consultant firm of McKinsey Company. They met and talked informally on Sunday, September 14. Next day Glennan sent over some descriptive material that Corson wanted, and the management executive began to consider the problem.

"Since our conversation on Sunday," Corson wrote Glennan on September 16, "I have reviewed the materials you handed me relative to the National Aeronautics and Space Administration. These materials, of course, and our conversation afford only a limited and preliminary understanding of the large problems you are confronted with in establishing promptly a new, large, and vitally important Federal Agency."[4]

---

[3] Ralph E. Cushman, special assistant, NASA Office of Administration, in conversation with the author.
[4] Letter Corson to Glennan, NASA historical files.

The problems?

As Corson saw them they were basically five in number:

1. The program.
2. Legislative and executive department relationships.
3. Transfer of aeronautical and space activities from other agencies.
4. Public information.
5. Staff.

Addressing himself to the last problem first, Corson assured administrator Glennan that McKinsey would help the agency with staff on a purely volunteer basis. Of course the McKinsey Company did not pretend to carry an expert imprimatur regarding scientific matters, but its function would be to set up the organization. In this, Corson suggested, he might voluntarily and without pay find such men as an administrative assistant to the administrator, a general counsel, an assistant administrator for management, and men for financing, personnel, contracting, and similar jobs. There would be no attempt to push people into NASA— Corson assured Glennan that he would offer two or more men for each job.

McKinsey, Corson said, was very much interested in taking on the NASA organization task, and would make a study, then a report by January 1. The cost would be in the neighborhood of $30,000 to $35,000 which would include the full time of one McKinsey man plus a third of Corson's own time until January 1. NASA would also have to assume the company's out-of-pocket expenses, such as secretarial services. The men discussed the plan again, and on

September 26 Corson wrote a formal letter offering the services for a fee of $33,000.[5]

The study began in October. It was completed by the end of the year, by Corson and John D. Young of McKinsey & Company. Robert Rosholt, in his *Administrative History of NASA*, indicates that the report was more or less a rationalization of what Glennan had already decided to do, and that its influence on NASA was relatively small.[6] Perhaps. But what the McKinsey Report of 1958 does represent is the independent thinking of a management consulting firm about the relationships between the space agency and business, the rest of government, and the public.

NASA, said the McKinsey report, represented something quite new in American government. It would be an agency of national scope, but one with very serious and far-reaching international concerns which would in their turn influence American foreign policy. NASA could expect to be under continual scrutiny in a way that almost no other agency was. The State and Defense departments and the Central Intelligence Agency had escape hatches of secrecy. NASA would be dealing in very sensitive areas, but without the sympathy given these others.

The agency would also have serious problems of approach and stance in its relationships with the scientific community, which was known to be extremely sensitive about its autonomy and dignity.

The reason for the creation of the new agency was to carry out the space program wanted by the American government and many of the American people. This assignment meant that the agency was to supervise the design,

[5] Letter Corson to Glennan, NASA files.
[6] Rosholt, p. 55.

development, construction, testing, launching, and operation of space vehicles. In all these fields the experience of government and business was extremely limited. To be sure, Maxime Faget and Caldwell Johnson of NACA had drawn up basic outlines for a manned ballistic satellite; they had figured configuration, equipment, heating, and structural matters. And a dozen major aircraft companies were working on space problems, constantly increasing their knowledge and sphere of activity.[7] But so new was the field that there were even serious questions about the general policy of procurement.

In 1959 the American government's procurement policies were still somewhat fuzzy. From its early history—actually from 1830 until World War I—procurement by the government had followed a strict path of buying from competing bidders in almost every field. Occasionally there were reasons why it was impossible to have competition of the straight price, specification, and delivery type; but unconventional procurements were always troublesome and usually subjected to severe scrutiny by Congress. In World War I the old procurement rules were thrown out the window, as government demanded and secured speedy delivery, sometimes under a cost-plus-profit figure or percentage.

For example, a shipbuilding company is employed to build Victory ships for the government. There is no problem about competitive bidding, because all companies are building all the ships they can manage. So the company agrees to build on a cost-plus-percentage of cost for profit. Ten per cent is figured. The company builds a ship for a million dollars. The profit is $100,000. But the company then relaxes, wastes materials, gets stuck by its suppliers at

[7] *This New Ocean*, p. 102.

high costs, and the second ship costs $1,250,000. All the better, the company increased its profit by $25,000, for 10 per cent of $1,250,000 is more than 10 per cent of $1 million. And that is what cost-plus-profit is all about. It is wasteful and can turn out to be dishonest. Except in emergencies there has never been any excuse for it. In the space program, when people were dealing with unknowns, attempts were made to justify the cost-plus, and it is still being considered, but it is a wasteful wrongheaded system.

After World War II, things never did get "back to normal" in the Department of Defense and other government agencies. Procurement was to be done by bidding if possible, by negotiation if necessary, and by purchase on the open market if *really* necessary. The law—the Armed Service Procurement Act—was really very simple. Unfortunately, its very simplicity gave rise to multifarious interpretations and problems. While the procurement act is set down on a single page of Congressional stationery, "the bookshelf of procurement practice takes up a good ten feet" (as Ralph Cushman put it, after many years of buying for NACA and working with NASA procurement).

McKinsey & Company's men saw this problem very clearly at a time when NASA was just in swaddling clothes: how should research and development contracts be let and administered in an area where there was very little experience, where there was only one customer, where the companies involved must feel out every step of the way? Although no pat answer could be given, the McKinsey report suggested a procedure.

First, men within NASA must identify and define the research and development needs. In other words, they must analyze a given problem thoroughly enough to prepare general specifications and requirements. This was necessary because the old practice of competitive bidding simply did not suit what might be called experimental contracting. What was crucial was the selection of organizations that might be asked to submit proposals. These contractors would have to be checked out early, to see that they had the potential capabilities to do the job.

Once these steps were taken, NASA officials must be prepared to evaluate the proposals made by industry. Two contractors studying the same problem might come up with very different approaches, even within the specifications and requirements. Thus NASA men must have technical knowledge, and even a bit of genius, to know where to go.

When the contract problem was resolved from a technical point of view, NASA must be able to negotiate and award the contract to some participant. Here price determination must be established. Was price to be the dominant factor?

And once the contract was let, NASA officials must administer it. In a simple bid of the old days, for, say, one hundred bulldozers, given specifications and requirements, price was just about the determining factor. But in the NASA administration, working with and creating new products that would have only limited use, price might not always be the controlling factor.

Administering a space contract could be a remarkably elaborate and fatiguing process. Take a space capsule: a primary contractor would be selected, and he would take on perhaps two hundred subcontracts to do his job. NASA's administrative officers would be responsible to see that the prime contractor did his job, but they had also best be alert to the capability of the subcontractors and they might be called on for spot checks. This new world meant quality

control, security control where security counted, management of appeals, and procedures for appeals in contract matters, for purchase approvals, and for running audits of the
program's cost. Finally, when the contract was finished,
NASA must have a procedure for product acceptance and
eventually for property disposal.[8]

Several things were obvious. One was that the Department of Defense was extremely able and experienced in the
field of negotiation and management of contracts. McKinsey
& Company recommended that the military be used to supplement the available NASA personnel. At the time, there
were not many experienced people in the new agency. As
Cushman put it, during the war and postwar years a whole
generation of procurement people had arisen who had only
on-the-job training in procurement. This limitation led to
what he termed a "quality approach to procurement" which
would still be felt ten years after the founding of NASA—
too much emphasis on the technicalities of clauses, too much
reliance on the "boilerplate" of contracts, and too little attention to the essence of the contract in question.[9]

From the point of view of an expanding agency, NACA
had suffered from many disabilities. The loose and comfortable relationship between NACA headquarters and the
research facilities was all very well for a small agency doing
a good deal of original research on aeronautical problems.
It would never do for a new big agency whose success or
failure would be judged by the hardware it put in the sky.
By hardware, the space men meant rockets and capsules
and satellites, and sometimes their various components.
Since it was expected that NASA would be spending a half

[8] McKinsey & Company, initial report, December 1958, NASA files.
[9] Cushman in conversation with the author.

billion dollars a year, much closer supervision seemed in order. NASA men must supervise launch pads. They would take over the Jet Propulsion Laboratory, or become involved in cost-plus-fee contracts with it. They would take over the Army's Ballistic Missile Agency and the Space Technology Laboratory. They would have new sites and new staffs.

To administer this complex, the National Space Act had established the positions of administrator and his deputy. But by McKinsey's estimate, these two were already spending about 60 per cent of their time with the President, other executive departments, Congress, and what McKinsey called "other externals." What was needed, said the report, was an inside man, an associate administrator for operations.

McKinsey also recommended far more detailed organization, some of which had been worked out already by a new internal NASA committee. The organization was to include a general counsel and directors of program planning, public information, international relations, and aeronautical and space research. There would be special divisions to study aerodynamics and flight mechanics, to carry on relations and arrange research contracts with universities, to study structures and materials, to study power plants, to manage contracts.

So complex was this new program that in the office of the director of business administration there would be seven division directors and three staff assistants.

The McKinsey report probably pleased no one except administrator Glennan, and in its complexities it made very heavy reading for all but professional administrators. But like the work of the Abbott committee before, it was a start in the attack on a complex problem of research and development of techniques and commodities that did not exist but must be invented.

Corson did help Glennan secure three senior administrative officials. One of these was John Johnson, who went into the agency as general counsel; another was Wesley Hjornevik, who became assistant to the administrator; and the third, Albert F. Siepert, became business manager, a position that included the functions of comptroller.

While McKinsey & Company was studying the problems of NASA organization, the world was moving on. By December, it was apparent that NASA was growing very rapidly and that not all its officials were familiar with its new acquisitions. John Corson suggested a study of the field operations of NASA. His suggestion was reviewed by a committee that included Siepert and Hjornevik, which decided that McKinsey ought to be hired on a much less ambitious project: to study the Jet Propulsion Laboratory that had belonged to the Army; and to determine whether, in view of the large number of contractor firms on the west coast, it would be a good idea to establish a western coordination office of NASA. The McKinsey suggestion had involved a contract of perhaps sixty-five to seventy thousand dollars, but for the work NASA wanted done the price would be around thirty-three thousand dollars. Everyone agreed that a long look must be taken at the Jet Propulsion Laboratory, if for no other reason than to learn from its experience. In these years, while NACA research centers were running projects that ran from forty to eighty thousand dollars, JPL's projects were sometimes twice as expensive and involved from three to six engineering man-years.[10]

Of the two studies, the more specific recommendations

[10] McKinsey-Glennan records in NASA historical files.

came in the case of the western coordination office. Back in 1939 NACA had established a small office in Los Angeles to deal with the large number of aeronautical firms located in that region. It started with two employees and by 1959 had only six. Now, North American Aviation was about to get the contract running into many millions of dollars for the 1,500,000-pound thrust jet engine, to say nothing of other contracts with other firms. And so some expert management was needed.

How badly it was needed would come to public attention in 1960 when Congress began checking on NASA contracting. The investigation, conducted by the House of Representatives Astronautics Committee, became a *cause célèbre*. And in the furor that developed, some of NASA's new problems were revealed: In 1958 a bidders' conference was held at NASA headquarters. Seven firms came to this meeting to hear NASA's general requirements. In October and November 1958, proposals were solicited from the seven companies. By November 25 (the deadline) six proposals were received. Each was then evaluated by a technical team and a management team, which presented their findings in meetings with Glennan and his major assistants, five men who made up NASA's source-selection board. The board recommended North American's Rocketdyne division for the job, and Glennan agreed to a round of negotiations with North American that he hoped would produce a contract.[11] Thus was established, with President Eisenhower's backing of administrator Glennan, the background for NASA's contracting procedures. Henceforth, NASA officials would feel more comfortable working out contracts with the Aerospace industry, for executive privilege had been upheld.

[11] Rosholt, pp. 99–100.

But if the privilege was upheld, so was the responsibility of NASA officials increased, for they did not have access to ordinary protections in contracting. From the outset, the experimental and sensitive nature of NASA's work made it necessary to keep contracts classified (against Russian and business espionage) and therefore to lean heavily on the experience of the Department of Defense, which was used to dealing in multi*billion*-dollar contracts of a highly classified nature. Since the public did not accept classification for NASA's space vehicles as readily as it would for defense rockets, the old bugaboo of "defense" was hauled out to protect what was essentially business competition. It is a problem that has never been solved satisfactorily, and may never be solved.

Administrator Glennan and his aides apparently sensed the problems that such secrecy could give rise to in the early months of 1959, when they were negotiating some very sensitive contracts, including the one with McDonnell Aviation which would result in the Mercury manned capsule for space. The McKinsey experts visited the Jet Propulsion Laboratory and the western offices and recommended the enlargement of the staff in Los Angeles to forty by 1960. Close management of the contracts was to be the watchword.

5

The Team Approach

The spacemen were to be tamed in the next few months. What was needed was some teamwork. Taking the military out of the space business (which has never really been accomplished) was to stop the wasteful competition. But the military never gives up power without a struggle: in 1971 the Air Force was still recruiting for its "Aerospace team." There were always to be plenty of conflicts, acute and underlying.[1] What was to be transferred and reorganized in the next few months was an immensely complex number of

[1] *Administrative History of NASA*, p. 46.

operations which had not before been grouped together. The whole concept of space exploration for its own sake—not as part of the military plan—was something so new that there simply were no guidelines.

NASA began assembling the parts of its body. First, of course, were the old NACA installations. The Navy gave up its Vanguard project, and plans were made to move that to the new Goddard Space Flight Center at Beltsville, Maryland. Eventually NASA would get some of the Naval Research Laboratory personnel, and other people scattered around the world who were engaged in tracking the earliest satellites for the Navy. The Air Force continued to do the physical work for two planned lunar probes, but responsibility was transferred to NASA. The Army Ballistic Missile Agency was working on two lunar probes and three satellite projects which also were transferred. Finally, the Air Force gave NASA a number of rocket-engine development programs, including a project that involved a study contract by North American Aviation for a million-pound-thrust rocket engine.

With all this, NASA realized that it must have the installations and people to do the work. So administrator Glennan began moving to get them. NASA had taken on the Jet Propulsion Laboratory, operated by California Institute of Technology for the Army. Glennan also wanted part of the Army Ballistic Missiles operation.

There came a rub.

The Army, in keeping with the arsenal concept, built its own military equipment. At the Redstone arsenal near Huntsville, Alabama, were concentrated people and equipment capable of designing, making, and launching big multistage rockets. By January 1958, this team had launched Explorer I, the first American satellite, demonstrating that government agencies could make their own products.[2]

But NASA was operating on a different theory, that the responsibility for the space program was a civilian matter, and that government's charge was to supervise and manage the program, making use of American industrial facilities. NASA, then, would require only a part of the development operations division of the arsenal, which meant a part of the team of men who worked under German rocket expert Wernher von Braun.

The Army did not want to give up von Braun, and it fought to keep its program, with one great success. The transfer was delayed and the team kept intact. Instead of becoming part of NASA in 1958, the von Braun team simply agreed to work for NASA as needed and remain part of the Army. The compromise saved the von Braun team but did not solve the administrative problems very well. By 1960 von Braun and forty-six hundred of his people went over to NASA, and their place became known as the George C. Marshall Space Flight Center.[3]

Meanwhile NASA went to work in a very peculiar and difficult realm, that of large scale procurement from private industry of things that simply did not exist. The whole point of NASA's inception was to develop a capability to explore space, which meant that everything would have to be started from idea and run through to a piece of equipment or a program. In the early days of NACA, procurement for this kind of material had been relatively simple. Ralph Cushman had been chief procurement officer, and his relations with business were relatively informal. For

[2] *Ibid.*, pp. 45–46.
[3] Von Braun and Ordway, p. 165.

example, at one point Cushman decided that NACA head-quarters people in the little agency's offices in Washington needed air conditioning. Now the building NACA occupied belonged to the General Services Administration, and no response to his requests was forthcoming. But Cushman was undeterred. He simply had window sets bought by centers at Cleveland and elsewhere, and then shipped to Washington. That was how things could be done in a small agency. On another occasion, when Cushman wanted a jet fighter plane for testing by NACA, he followed Air Force General Curtis LeMay around the corridors of the Pentagon until he got one assigned to him. That was intergovernmental relations in the good old days. And when Cushman was annoyed with the rates being charged the NACA laboratories outside Cleveland by the Cleveland light and power company, he simply refused to pay the bill until the company agreed to renegotiate. That was government-industry relations.[4]

But Cushman was used to thinking in terms of thousands and an occasional million. It was apparent from the beginning that NASA would be dealing in the billions.

What NASA was jumping into was a complicated scientific, engineering, and management puzzle with which the armed forces had been struggling since the end of World War II, in connection with rockets and missile performance —and NASA was adding the new element of controlled manned flight.

The development of one aerospace company shows a good deal about the problem. Early in the 1950's the United States Air Force was concerned about the development and rapid production of a ballistic missiles system for national

[4] Ralph Cushman in interview with author.

defense. It was suspected, even feared, that the Russians had a technological system that was much more efficient than ours. Several Defense Department committees considered the problem. They went back to the airplane to get some of the answers to their questions, specifically to study how the Air Force had managed the program for development of the complicated B-58 bomber, the first large U.S. supersonic aircraft. Here existed the problems of propulsion, aerodynamics, airframe development, plus all the new problems (such as cooling) connected with supersonic flight.

Until this time, the Air Force had always held the responsibility for "systems integration." That is, the military had made contracts with different business firms to build the airframe and the components of the aircraft. The integration of all these parts to make a plane had been the responsibility of the military men themselves.

But with the B-58 the complexities of production and engineering were so enormous that the Air Force decided to give the "systems integration" problem to a contractor. The job fell to the air frame contractor, the Convair division at Fort Worth, although the Air Force kept the responsibility for the propulsion system, which was under contract to General Electric. This was in 1951.

Studying the difficulties of the ballistics missiles program several years later, Air Force chiefs realized the importance of "systems management." But in missile development the Air Force, like everyone else, was on new ground. Many of the skills and technical advances necessary for missiles were quite outside the old aeronautical concepts. And there was a hurry, because intelligence reports indicated the Russians were ahead in missile development. In

1953, Air Force officials considered advancing the priority of the Atlas missile program ahead of the B-58 (the latest conventional bombing weapon).

How was this to be done? The Air Force appointed a scientific survey committee to see if some prime contractor might be able to take full responsibility for integration of the four major systems involved in the missile—the nose cone, air frame, propulsion, and guidance systems. This (von Neumann) committee found that *not a single* prime contractor in the aerospace business could handle the integration of the four systems.[5] And this is how the Thompson-Ramo-Wooldridge firm was formed.

In 1953 two vice-presidents of the Hughes Aircraft Company of California saw how serious were becoming the complexities of military electronic engineering. They were Simon Ramo and Dean Wooldridge. They put up $6,750 each, and started the Ramo-Wooldridge Corporation, using as offices a converted barber shop in Los Angeles. Their dream was a limited one: they wanted to secure for themselves some of the business of designing and manufacturing electronic equipment for the military services.

But by the summer of 1954 the Air Force's Scientific Advisory Committee reported that there was no industrial firm in the United States capable of taking on a systems management program.

The Air Force turned to the universities then, but after a few weeks it was apparent that no university had the combination of management and technical personnel and time to supervise so broad a program as missile develop-

5 Hearings, Subcommittee of the Committee on Government Operations, HR 86th Congress, 1st session, Organization and Management of Missile Programs, pp. 23–29.

ment. But Ramo-Woolridge did exist (with eighteen employees at the end of 1953), and the skills were there in embryo.

In May, the Air Force signed a systems management contract with Ramo-Wooldridge. At first the job was "technical management." Almost immediately Ramo-Wooldridge's employment rose to 281 skilled persons. A year later it was up to 1,156. In 1957 it rose to 3,269. That year Ramo-Wooldridge had management problems of its own, and merged with Thompson Products Inc., of Cleveland, which had advanced $500,000 in the early days to get the company started.

As time went on, Ramo-Wooldridge took on more responsibility, because the "systems management" system worked very well indeed. The firm built up a competence in all four systems and then was able to design them. In this sense, they became the brains of the Air Force. They did not select contractors. They did not build the parts. They did give technical advice to the Air Force. Soon they were doing planning for ballistic missiles and for space technology. As planners, they developed considerable power; the Air Force began consulting the company about contractors and designs.[6]

By 1957, Thompson-Ramo-Wooldridge was the wonder boy of the space business. That first basic contract with the Air Force had brought the firm a fee of $668,000, or 14.3 per cent of the estimated cost of the contracts to be supervised. The high percentage was justified by the Air Force because of the skills needed and the fast build-up required of the company. Comparable fees were paid until 1957, however, and TRW was then rolling in success. Assets of the com-

[6] *Ibid.* Also Harvard Business School internal document EA–550, 1967.

pany at the end of 1967 were $29 million, and shareholders' equity (stock, surplus, and retained earnings) came to $9,145,540.[7] Ramo and Wooldridge were each drawing $50,-000 a year in salary besides. Thompson industries actually controlled (owned) the company, but Ramo and Wooldridge were operating it.

With the Thompson ownership of the company came a change in approach. In the beginning, Ramo-Wooldridge was a consulting firm which agreed not to compete for contracts to build parts for the missiles on which it consulted. That was fair enough. But with the new system, the company had a capability of manufacture and wanted to exercise it. The firm set up a subsidiary called Space Technology Laboratories to do the old consulting work, and competed for contracts. It won a subcontract for the design and fabrication of the Titan missile program, and another contract for development and production of an intelligence data handling system, competing against the Radio Corporation of America, Eastman Kodak, and International Business Machines. The aerospace industry began to complain. So loud was the complaint that by 1959 Thompson-Ramo-Wooldridge was forced to create a new, nonprofit subsidiary called Aerospace Corporation. About a fifth of the old Space Technology Laboratories people went into this corporation, and TRW became for the first time an independent business firm, competing in the open marketplace for orders and jobs. Ramo and Wooldridge had taken their skills and $6,750 each, and in four years had run their fortunes to around $3 million each, while earning salaries that began at $37,500 and rose to $50,000 per year. In the hearings before the House of Representatives subcommittee on government op-

[7] Organization and Management of Missile Programs Hearings, p. 694.

erations in the winter of 1959, California Representative Chet Holafield noted that he was "deeply impressed." So were many others.

Even before NASA came into being, then, it was apparent in the aeronautical industry that the space business was becoming something big. But at this time (1958) the emphasis still was on simply moving into space. Keeping a satellite in orbit and providing a habitable environment for humans were still very much in the planning stage.

One of the most successful of all American space programs was then coming along very nicely. It would wind up as the Tiros program, involving a satellite that would not fail to orbit and would return very useful information to the earth. Here was the first American space venture that could be shown to be truly useful to humanity. And how it got started is a story of business and government in partnership—and some perplexing problems.

The Navy and the Air Force had been considering satellites since the mid-1940's and had conducted several studies of them. A study undertaken for the Air Force's Rand Corporation by S. M. Greenfield and W. W. Kellogg demontrated the theoretical feasibility of weather reconnaissance from a satellite, based largely on analysis of photographs taken from V-2 rockets fired at White Sands late in the 1940's.[8] The Greenfield-Kellogg report excited some meteorologists, among them Dr. J. Bjerknes, who had also studied such photos and found that cloud pictures taken from above could be very valuable in weather prediction.

[8] The above and much of the following information comes from an unpublished study of the history of the Tiros project prepared for the Brookings Institution in 1966.

Meanwhile, the Radio Corporation of America had been doing some work of its own in the satellite field. RCA had also done work for RAND in 1949 and had worked on what became the Greenfield-Kellogg report.

RCA continued its studies. In 1951 it teamed up with the Bell Aircraft Company to take a study contract (one of three awarded that year) to propose a new reconnaissance system for the Air Force. With this contract, RCA was able to keep eighteen scientists and engineers occupied in the study of the satellite and use of television for various monitoring purposes. Here, of course, RCA was very lucky, for the greatest problem of industry in developing space capability is the expense of maintaining a study team of specialists. Spurred by profit, stopped by loss, American industry can support nonpractical or "pure" research and development only in a limited way, and then only when there promises to be some application that eventually can be peddled.

In this Air Force study, RCA and Bell came out first—speaking technically. But here was revealed one of the major anomalies of the space business: they did not get the contract from the Air Force to develop the reconnaissance system. The reason was that Lockheed Aircraft Corporation had a workable system from its study, as well as a long, good record in the building of aircraft for the government. Using RCA and Bell, the Air Force would have two contractors to deal with. The military men preferred the known quantity. (Eventually, the Lockheed contract produced the SAMOS satellite.)

Now with a team of eighteen specialists, RCA was faced with a problem: could it support the cost of this study alone, and if so, for how long? The answer was to find another outlet, and in this connection the RCA men went to Wernher von Braun at the Army Ballistic Missile Agency, long before the NASA days. Von Braun had been interested in satellites for many years. He had persuaded the Army to undertake a program with the office of the Chief of Naval Research as a partner. But the Naval Research Laboratory's project Vanguard had knocked that plan out in 1955, and von Braun was burning to work on a satellite and was developing the rocket techniques to do so. Unlike some in Huntsville, von Braun was also business-oriented; from the days in Germany, he had accepted the principle of business participation in the rocket and space programs.

The RCA men came to Huntsville at just the right time. Soon they secured a study contract from the Army Ballistics Missiles Agency to test the feasibility of the satellite TV idea, using a variation of the Redstone rocket (Jupiter C). Von Braun was able to get the plan through by claiming it as the basic study for a satellite to locate military targets. It would be a twenty-pound rod-shaped spacecraft.[9]

This contract ran out at about the time the military men developed a better rocket for the purpose, so RCA secured a second study contract to work on a Juno II rocket. There were new technical problems to be overcome including changing the shape of the satellite. A new element was added. RCA would build the satellite, the von Braun organization would mate it to the rockets, and the Signal Corps would manage it in space. Herbert Butler of the Signal Corps Research and Development Laboratory at Fort Monmouth, N.J., became the overseer of the satellite project for the government.

[9] H. I. Butler and S. Sternberg, *TIROS—The System and Its Evaluation*, IRE Transactions on Military Electronics, April-July 1960, p. 249.

RCA was still operating on a study basis, making barely enough money on the program to support it. By spring the Defense Department had changed its mind again, and the reconnaissance idea was out: the Air Force was to have that space responsibility. Von Braun, however, secured the support of Roy Johnson's Advanced Research Projects Agency to change back to a weather satellite, and the program went on.

Now it had become more than a study contract, for RCA was building the satellite, or "hardware," as the space-men came to call it. In 1958 there were more changes. The rocket was changed (to the Juno IV booster), and the satellite could be larger. So it was redesigned. Now it became Television Infrared Observation Satellite, or TIROS. So RCA was working on a 270-pound satellite which carried two television cameras to photograph the earth's cloud cover.

In October, the Defense Department made another change, from a Jupiter-based rocket system to a Thor—which meant RCA again had to modify the satellite.

This was what they called Research and Development. Originally the program for 1958–59 had been estimated to cost about six million dollars, including the RCA contract and the amount allocated to Huntsville for the rockets. The first changes added $900,000 to the plan, and the second, major, changes, more than three million dollars. So this bit of research and development was to cost $10 million, or an overrun (as the accountants described it) of about 70 per cent of the original budget.

In a way it is remarkable that either TIROS or the RCA contracts survived the next few months, when the project went from one change to another, winding up in 1959 in

the hands of NASA, with Herbert Butler and others trans-
ferring to the civilian space agency to manage the show. But
the RCA program survived. It called for one prototype
satellite, two flight-qualified satellites, spare parts for two
others. For this, some seven million dollars had been committed by the government in a succession of steps. The
project's survival was probably due to the pliability and
sheer ability of Roger Warner, project manager for TIROS
under the Defense Department, who saw most of the
changes through to the NASA stage. Finally TIROS management ended up at the Goddard Space flight Center
under Dr. William Stroud and his staff, with RCA still hang-
ing on as contractor.

By this time, 1959, the program was called NIMBUS,
and it was estimated that it would last for five years—but
not that the same satellites would be used, or that RCA
would necessarily have the contracts. In 1960 NASA got
$7,200,000 of the nearly eleven million dollars asked, and the
program continued.

In April 1960, the first TIROS satellite was launched. It
was a stunning success, producing good, usable weather pictures on a regular basis for meteorologists. The next year a
special committee proposed the establishment of the program as an operational space program. There would be
more research and development, to be sure, but by 1964 the
program was to be stabilized, and by 1966 at least two spacecraft would be continuously in orbit taking weather data.
President Kennedy put the final seal of approval on the program in 1961 in his special space message to Congress, asking for $75 million for weather satellites.

By the summer of 1961 the third TIROS craft had
been launched, and the cost, paid to RCA, had been $9,800,-

000. RCA by this time had developed a rather extensive facility for this work at its laboratories in New Jersey, and both company and government had contributed testing and research facilities not precisely in the terms of the contract. The third TIROS ended NASA's support funds, but the program was so successful that Congress authorized another $20 million to extend the program for another four launches, at four-month intervals. RCA's Astro-Electronics Products Division of Princeton was to make the spacecraft, and RCA's Service Corporation was to operate the reading stations.

In 1962, as the scientists were beginning to talk about the "operational" program, difficulties developed in the control and camera systems and in the panel of solar cells by which the sun recharged the satellite's batteries and made possible long and continual operation.

For RCA, the contract with NASA produced some valuable sidelines. Based on its successful performance, the Navy asked RCA to make studies for the requirements of a tactical weather satellite. RCA was also still involved in the NIMBUS program, going through a series of serious difficulties that caused all contractors trouble. In this program General Electric had responsibility for controls and spacecraft integration and testing, while RCA worked up other systems including solar power and cameras. Both major contractors were a year to two years late with certain components.

The basic difficulty in the NIMBUS program was that there was no industrial contractor. Goddard Space Flight Center could in one sense be called the prime contractor, and that was not much liked by industry, which now preferred to have the responsibility and the authority.

One of the problems was simply getting information

around to those who needed it. For example, if RCA made a change in an electrical circuit, the news was sent to Goddard, which then sent it to General Electric, which was responsible for spacecraft integration. That method certainly did not work very well: eventually the General Accounting Office said such failures caused the economic waste of two million dollars' worth of work by General Electric.

Project director Stroud wanted Goddard Space Flight Center in actual fact to be the prime contractor, but because this was a violation of NASA's basic approach to the space business, administrator Glennan did not accept it totally. Thus arose a system that was neither one thing nor the other. Stroud suggested that GE, as the integrator, maintain an office at Goddard Space Flight Center. GE did not do it. That created more confusion. So the big NIMBUS project languished, and the smaller TIROS project grew stronger. Throughout, the Weather Bureau (as a prime user) and the space agency had quarreled over the details of the NIMBUS project.

After much bureaucratic infighting, in 1964 the Weather Bureau and NASA made a new agreement for satellite control and use, and the TIROS Operational System (TOS) was put into effect, with RCA again working as the prime contractor because it had the technical team, the knowledge, and the facilities to do the job. The TIROS program continued until nine of these satellites had been launched. The tenth was then placed in a sun-synchronous orbit, which increased its stability and thus its usefulness to scientists. And as of 1969, as the TOS program was under way, RCA still held two major contracts with NASA to design, build, and provide operational support for TIROS satellites, contracts that were worth more than $58 million cumulatively, with $11,500,000 or so to go.[10]

By this time the Astro-Electronics division of RCA had expanded considerably. A major facility had been built at Hightstown, New Jersey, where millions of dollars' worth of government equipment necessary for the testing of the satellites had been shipped.

Each year the TIROS program became more complex. As the operational TOS plan was made part of the system, it became even more complicated, for each of the twelve spacecraft that had been launched represented changes and improvements in patterns and work. The newest program called for High Resolution Infrared Radiation, which meant the use of sensors that could provide readings on *night time* cloud cover, delicate thermometers for measuring the earth's heat, better television and cameras, measurements of the temperature of the atmosphere. All this added up to potential for far more accurate data to help earth-bound meteorologists study atmospheric patterns and predict weather changes. It was planned to put up synchronous meteorological satellites with spacecraft in earth-synchronous stationary orbits, thus permitting continuous observation of the earth and the ability to note hourly changes in cloud patterns around the earth. With some two hundred reporting stations around the world (established with ESSA-2 satellites), the system was becoming refined.[11]

Looking into 1970, then, RCA had been closely associated with NASA and its predecessors in the space program for a dozen years and more. The problems of TIROS

[10] *NASA Procurement Program Policies and Trends Handbook,* 1969.
[11] Robert M. Rados, "The Evolution of the TIROS Meteorological Satellite Operational System," Bulletin of the American Meteorological Society, May 1967, pp. 326–337.

had been solved, one by one, from the days of Roger Warner in ARPA to those of Herbert Butler as director of operational satellites at the Goddard Space Center—always with the cooperation of government and business employees. A hundred million dollars had been spent on the program, much of that going to RCA in costs and fees.

And by 1969 several patterns had emerged, presenting new problems in the maturing space business. One problem was lead time, which worried the officials at Goddard Space Center considerably.[12]

Lead time meant the time it took from the moment when Congress had approved a development in the TIROS program, including allocation of the money in the NASA budget, and the officers in the field and at headquarters had agreed on a program and were ready to move. From the opening moment until the contract was signed it took an average of four hundred days to secure all the necessary action. This long time meant that the technicians had to be constantly planning far ahead of themselves simply to achieve their scientific and engineering ends in the face of bureaucratic pressures. The bureaucratic pressures grew for several reasons, not the least of them the constant worry of the NASA officials involved in procurement lest they be brought up short by Congress. NASA being primarily a research and development agency, almost everything it did was new and even experimental, and Congress has always liked to take close looks at such programs, particularly when they are funded by government and carried out by industry. More particularly is this true when, as with NASA, the old pro-

[12] The following is based largely on discussions with H. I. Butler, Director of Operational Satellites at Goddard Space Flight Center; Michael L. Garbacz, TIROS-TOS-ESSA Program Manager, and Harvey M. Kennedy, Jr., of the Office of Industry Affairs.

curement practices of "competitive bidding" simply could not be adjusted to the needs of the space program.

In practical terms, the lead-time problem meant that after all the NASA officials who must be consulted on changes had been consulted about developing a vertical temperature profiling instrument as part of the new TIROS package, it was a year before the contract to produce the instrument got to RCA.

Another problem presented itself. After so long an association with RCA, the NASA officials in charge of TIROS were very conscious of the exclusive nature of their relationship with the company, and not entirely comfortable in it. Some wondered if such a long-term relationship on one basic project did not make the company tend to relax. To be sure, there was the asset of a close working understanding between government supervisors and industry producers. It was useful to be able to telephone or write a letter and know exactly whom one was addressing and what areas could be most fruitfully discussed. It was valuable to know the strengths, and even the limitations, of the people and company. But there was always nagging doubt, because Congress accepts only begrudgingly the Defense Department's concept of negotiated contracts with "sole sources" (the only source of supply). And within the agency NASA people are constantly called upon to justify the "sole source" concept. (In every contract this is mandatory and in discussion of changes it nearly always comes up.)

Each time a change in the TIROS spacecraft was discussed, the NASA managers and scientists also considered changing prime contractors. Always the discussion raised the same question: why not put up the program for competitive bidding?

Then came the facing of the answers. RCA certainly had developed a competence in the field, and was familiar with the history of the project. It was very important to know what changes had been tried and failed, what changes had been discussed and discarded, what studies had been accepted and found not feasible. (Herbert Butler, for example, recalled one technical study which had been let out to contract years ago and found unfeasible—but every year or so some new member of the TIROS team would bring up the idea. Were there no known history of the project, mistake and useless study could be repeated over and over again.) The problem was not a minor one, particularly with the constant change in NASA management which began in 1969, as the agency came to the end of its "new" status and began losing people to other government agencies that offered quicker advancement. There had always been the problem of attrition, for from the industry standpoint the space business is one of the most volatile. From the government standpoint new agencies always tend to rob old ones of secondary managers. It was obviously valuable to keep as much stability as possible.

Physically, it was very difficult for NASA to consider disengagement from RCA in the TIROS program. From RCA's point of view its corporate investment was very large, including facilities it had put up at Hightstown that would not easily be converted to other uses. From the government's point of view it had invested millions of dollars in vibration testing equipment, vacuum thermal testing equipment, and other special tools that were needed to see that the satellite vehicles met specifications. If a new contractor were brought into the field, what would happen? TIROS was still operational. The equipment was needed at Hightstown. If a new contractor was chosen—say General Electric or Westinghouse, which would have the capability—then the government facilities, as well as the industrial facilities, must be duplicated, a highly wasteful process.

And there was still another problem, that of "funding." From the moment of the decision that a new idea is worth pursuing, it probably takes as many as four years to put an object into space, and NASA administration and the Congress work on a fiscal-year basis. Only a new program is likely to receive the gentle understanding treatment that will allow the funds necessary for a four-year lag.

So, year after year before the NASA budgeteers came around to the Office of Space Science and Applications, the discussions about TIROS were held, the changes were planned and approved at the management levels, and RCA remained the contractor. There was something here to be learned about the complications of the space business.

6

The Way It Was

NASA took so severe a shellacking from Congress and the public for its techniques of acquisition that it developed a procurement organization as thick as a protective shell—and for the same purposes.

Indeed, one major bureau of the agency is concerned with nothing else; that is the Office of Industry Affairs, headed in 1970 by assistant administrator George J. Vecchietti (acting), who also doubled as director of procurement. Previously the offices had been separate but old NASA lost its assistant administrator in this field to new HUD. It is instructive to see just who helps George Vecchietti, in terms of jobs.

Under the director of procurement are a deputy and executive assistant and a special assistant. There is a special officer to assist industry. There is a small-business adviser, a director of policy and administration. Under the director of policy and administration (this is procurement only, now) is an assistant director of procurement policy and administration. Under him is a policy and regulations division chief, and under him a pricing division chief, a contract administration division chief, and a research grants and contracts division chief. Equal to the policy man is an assistant director of procurement for administration. Under him is a surveys division chief, an inquiries division chief, a staff operations division chief, an administrative officer, a procurement office shared with other agencies.

Equal to the policy and administrations officer is the procurement operations director, who has three major assistants. One is the assistant director of contract review. Another is the assistant director for manned programs. He, in turn, has two assistants, one for Apollo procurement (manned space flight) and one for advanced missions. These of course are both chiefs, like all the others, and have Indians under them.

Equal to these chiefs is the assistant director of procurement for science, technology, and tracking programs, and he has three chiefs for three programs, each with Indians.

Now, under the assistant administrator for Industry Affairs, and equal to the procurement director in theory, are a chairman of a board of inventions and contributions, and a staff director; a cost reduction office, with a director, assistant director for internal programs and one for external programs; a labor relations office with a director and deputy; a reliability and quality assurance office with a director and three chiefs—one for evaluation and analysis, one for plans and policy, one for technical applications—and various Indians.

This organization, it might seem, would handle every conceivable problem that could arise between the government agency and the business world. But no, the Office of Industry Affairs is only a part of the business relations office of the space agency. Very high on the NASA list, up by the administrator in the table (ensconced in the same suite of offices in fact) is a board of contract appeals, and not far away is a contract adjustment board. Under the Office of General Counsel, there is a deputy and an associate, and an assistant general counsel for procurement matters.

Within the Office of Organization and Management, which is roughly co-equal to the Office of industry Affairs, there is a whole headquarters contracts division with a director, deputy, chief of support staff, four negotiations branch chiefs and a contract administration branch chief— all with Indians.

In the Office of Administration there is a contract finance and accounting branch chief.

One very important part of the agency (established after the disastrous fire at Cape Canaveral) is an Office of Special Contracts Negotiation and Review, headed by an assistant administrator, with two assistants and two assistants to the assistants.

The Office of Tracking and Data Acquisition has its own procurement support man. The Office of Space Science and Applications has its own procurement support officer in the program review and resources management staff. And so does the Office of Advanced Research and Technology.

It must be remembered that, in addition to this complicated organization and interweaving of officials, some of the officers very much concerned with procurement, such as Ralph Cushman, the old NACA procurement man, are not listed at all in this category, but appear as assistant assistant administrators or deputy assistant administrators. The test is sometimes not what the table says, but what the people do.[1]

The object of the foregoing list of titles is not to denigrate the work of the people who acquire goods and services for NASA, but to give an indication of the complexities of this program and of the reason for the long lead time between the approval of an acquisition by the technicians and the actual signing of a contract.

In short, Congressional and public criticism of NASA made its officers supersensitive, and like bureaucrats anywhere, very much concerned with the protection of their skins. Once upon a time Ralph Cushman could sneak those air conditioners into Washington for NACA workers under Research and Development. He was caught up by the General Accounting Office in this one time, by the way, which is another story of interest in comparing new and old days. After Cushman had finagled a number of air conditioners for Washington, his subprocurement officer at Cleveland's research center got careless. It would be so much more simple and efficient, said the subofficer, to have the manufacturers ship the air conditioners direct from factory to Washington. So this was done, and the General Accounting

[1] Table of Organization NASA, summer 1969.

Office auditors came around the next year and asked Cushman why?

Because the air conditioners were needed, said Cushman.

All right, said the accountant. Where was the authorization for air conditioners for the Washington office?

Of course there was no authorization.

So the subprocurement officer, who had signed the order for shipment, was presented with a bill for several thousand dollars for air conditioners.

The officer called Cushman on the telephone, obviously upset. But Cushman, lawyer and experienced civil servant, was not. He called the government accountants. So the air conditioners were several thousands of dollars, right? Right. And they belonged to the procurement officer in Cleveland, right? Right. And he was supposed to pay for them? Right!

All right, said Cushman, then he would pay for them, just as soon as the government paid the Cleveland officer the rent for using the machines for the year past. And did the government wish to continue to rent the machines, did it wish to purchase them, or would it prefer that the Cleveland man sold them off elsewhere?

The government accountants somehow managed to adjust the NACA budget satisfactorily without bothering either Cushman or his Cleveland assistant any further.[2]

But while some of the Old NACA Hands might be willing even now to cut corners thus, the system works against them constantly. Acquisition by government is big business, and it would be too much to expect it to be performed simply.

[2] Ralph Cushman in conversation with author.

In terms of procurement NASA always has operated under the same conditions as the Department of Defense. With one vast difference: the Defense Department is able to conceal errors in judgment under the label of secrecy, whereas relatively little of NASA's buying is in classified areas. It was determined a long time ago, under the Eisenhower Administration, that NASA would operate very largely in the glare of publicity, and generally speaking the officials of the agency have respected that directive in principle and practice. In one way or another the public has come to know about the conditions of acquisition and performance of most of the big NASA contracts, except possibly where missiles, and thus defense, are directly concerned.

The Armed Forces Procurement Act, which applies to NASA, goes back to the days when it was discovered that in research and development which covers space exploration as well as defense work, the old competitive bidding just did not work—for the big items.

One of the first actions taken by administrator Glennan in 1959 was to appoint a former Air Force procurement specialist as head of NASA's procurement department. Other buying people also came from the Air Force. That has been very much a pattern since.

Always the first step in an acquisition for NASA was the preparation of a procurement request by the technicians in charge of the program involved. It would include descriptions of the materials wanted and information about the possible field of suppliers or contractors. The easy matter, then, was the item that simply could be bought "off the shelf." Unfortunately, when NASA began dealing with space very little could be bought. It was possible to buy trucks and typewriters, but not satellites or nearly any of their components. It was not very long before NASA was spending ninety dollars on contracts for things that had to be worked out (R and D), as opposed to ten dollars for over-the-counter materials.

Now for small business, it was always relatively simple. As every businessman who wants any government contracts knows, the Department of Commerce maintains its own daily newspaper. The *Commerce Business Daily* consists solely of information about government procurement requests, foreign business opportunities, surplus property sales, services, and supplies. A look at one issue of *Commerce Business Daily* and a few contracts indicates why a typical NASA contract almost always had to be negotiated.[3]

Goddard Space Flight Center advertised intent to contract for "a feasibility study of a hydrezine electrolysis injector." Requests for package (this meant general specifications and work plan) would be honored as long as the supply lasted. Anyone who felt he had the capability, in other words, could bid.

George C. Marshall Space Flight Center put out a slightly different notice: "Negotiations will be conducted," it said, "with North American Rockwell Corp. for non-severable continuation and expansion of a program entitled 'Study of the effects of point defects and dislocations on the stress corrosion susceptibility of aluminum alloys.' "

Now this second contract was a study contract, made with a very important NASA supplier for a very special purpose. It was to be negotiated. It would not be thrown up for bids, and no other space contractor need apply. The study had been begun by North American Rockwell and it would so continue.

[3] *Commerce Business Daily*, July 30, 1969.

Most of NASA's contracts followed that order from the beginning. To be sure, NASA hoped to make work available to small business, and its contracting brochure opens with a discussion of this. But the real hope of small business firms was always to link up with a prime contractor and thus get a share of the subcontracting. Some bids were formally advertised for in the old government way, but not very many.[4]

Obviously, the RCA contract for the TIROS program (for example) had to be a part of the negotiation process for NASA. In the old Defense Department days, no one was sure precisely what would be wanted, and even when NASA took over the program many changes were made all the way along the line. TIROS I proved the feasibility of obtaining and using pictures of cloud cover. By TIROS 3, however, the scientists were making operational use of the data and considering storm warnings and hurricane observation. By TIROS 6, the demand was for continuous northern and southern hemispheric coverage. The scientists demanded of TIROS 8 direct readout to more than fifty stations all over the world, and TIROS 9 had to be able to cover the complete sunlit earth daily.[5]

These changes came steadily. What made it possible to make them and still retain an orderly contract was a new management development known as contract administration, which grew to create specialists in the field. In the beginning, the TIROS contract was a Cost-Plus-Fixed-Fee (CPFF) contract, and RCA was guaranteed their fee. But as time went on, NASA decided that the conditions were such that incentives would be useful, which meant that

[4] *Selling to NASA*, pp. 4–13.
[5] Rados, *op. cit.*, p. 337.

the contract was changed to a Cost-Plus-Incentive-Fee basis (CPIF). Dates were established for deliveries. If the company beat the dates, it earned incentive feees.

Among other reasons for the change was the belief that the items needed were not susceptible to complete description, and the sooner the problems could be solved, the more money RCA might make from the contract. (RCA has never earned the optimum provided in the incentive-fee system.)

Where the contract administrators come in, in the management departments of NASA headquarters, is to oversee the incentives. Since NASA is a decentralized agency, the thirteen outer offices and space centers each has its own purchasing executives and procedures, based on the master headquarters plan, but headquarters reviews all these matters eventually. And then there are the quality control overseers, who study the contractor's work and obligations to see if he is earning his fees and incentive payments, and who report back to the administrators. In the formative NASA years this program was rather simple. As time went on and the requirements of NASA changed, it grew ever more complicated.

One aspect of contracting for NASA which seems more genteel than most is that of the university work programs. NASA has always had university connections—it was regarded from the beginning as a scientifically oriented agency —even though in 1969's rumpuses about the Apollo program, scientists expressed disenchantment with the prominence given engineering over scientific requirements. The university work programs began in 1959, with an expenditure of 3.6 million dollars. That is not very much, but these dollars represented almost entirely study contracts in a highly technical field.

For a time (in the 1960's) university programs played a very heavy role in NASA's affairs. And the JPL, or Jet Propulsion Lab, still is operated by the California Institute of Technology for a fee of about one and a quarter million dollars which goes into the university's general fund.

JPL goes back to the old von Karman days but became most active in the space program after World War II, moving into research in jet propulsion technology, rocket aerodynamics, and electronic guidance and control of these systems. During and after the Korean war the laboratory worked for the Army on rockets. It also worked with Wernher von Braun's force, and it helped produce Explorer I, the first American satellite.

When NASA took over JPL, the laboratory's work centered upon unmanned exploration of space—the moon and the planets particularly—and also on the manned space program. JPL was think-tank as well as manufacturer and contract supervisor. Some scientific devices were built right in the laboratory. But JPL also contracted with Hughes Aircraft Company to build a major part of the Surveyor satellite, or rather, suggested that NASA contract with Hughes, and then supervised the contract for NASA. JPL also let out other subcontracts, and in this sense was a prime contractor with NASA. The fee JPL receives is basically one-half of one per cent of the total amount of money it expends. From the standpoints of Cal Tech and NASA the arrangement continued to be sound, because JPL not only brought very high-quality scientific minds to bear on NASA problems, but also used university resources and exposed the students of Cal Tech to the NASA program.[6] If

[6] Hearings before a subcommittee of the Committee on Government Operations, U.S. House of Representatives, 87th Congress, 2nd session, "Systems Development and Management," pp. 1735–1750.

it was something of a cost-plus contract, nobody complained very seriously until 1970.

A few contracts were subsequently worked out with other universities to provide support plans and studies for NASA. Massachusetts Institute of Technology, for example, would work on inertial guidance problems. But for the most part, university participation came through the Office of Research Grants and Contracts, which at first made all the arrangements for work with nonprofit institutions. Later, in the decentralization of NASA, this program was changed —and became more complicated.[7]

The point is that NASA contracting, with universities as well as industry, is now extremely complex because of the nature of the American economy. In the 1970's even universities are constantly fighting for money and take a business approach to many problems. No matter where one looks in the space effort, the profit motive emerges as very strong. For this reason NASA has chosen to surround itself with a mysterious and complex purchasing system, but in all fairness it is hard to see how such complexity can be reduced, given the shrinking number of prime contractors, the "national defense" red tape that is pulled out on many occasions, and the wolfish nature of business. Unless there is a change in the whole approach to the space effort which takes it out of the business field, complex purchasing arrangements will continue to be the rule.

[7] The conclusion is the author's. The information comes from Rosholt, pp. 128–29.

7

Who Gets the Contract Anyhow?

In 1959, prodded by Senator Stuart Symington and his Senate investigating committee, administrator Glennan pushed through a long-range space plan for NASA. It could not be a very perfect plan, because too little was known about the instruments that would be needed. But it was a "ten-year plan" calling for men in space and considerable lunar exploration. The cost would run about $1,500 million a year, and for that money the United States would regain its position of leadership in applied science, which had slipped badly with the Russian development of the atomic bomb, the hydrogen bomb, and the Sputniks.

Obviously the space business was going to become a very big business in America, although how big was not realized even by the basic airframe companies and the managers of the industry. Skepticism came with some justification: as late as 1968 the space business accounted for only about 10 per cent of the aerospace industry's total business. But a decade earlier some companies saw the handwriting on the wall, and the most advanced of them, as noted, had seen it ten or fifteen years before the formation of NASA.

Big rockets were being built by the von Braun group and others. Space technology was moving rapidly in 1958. In connection with the long-term planning, new subjects such as the life sciences and environmental problems were getting serious attention, and special forces were established within NASA to study them.

But among the several problems that had to be solved, if NASA were to carry out its ten-year program for space exploration, was the development of a very powerful rocket engine. In 1958 the space agency addressed itself seriously to the problem.

Rocketry had come along since the early days. Early in the 1950's the Rocketdyne division of North American Aviation had modified the Navaho booster engine, helping to create the Redstone, which was the big, powerful rocket used at the beginning of NASA's days. In 1956 Rocketdyne worked on the engine system of the Atlas ICBM, while Convair worked out the airframe. The rocket had a thrust of 360,000 pounds. When NASA was formed, among other assets it received was a study contract signed between the Air Force and North American Aviation for a one-million-pound-thrust rocket engine.[1]

[1] *This New Ocean*, pp. 1–125.

North American had prospered and suffered in the space and aeronautical business since 1928, when it was founded as a holding company. In 1934 the company was reorganized as a manufacturer, and E. H. Kindelberger became president. That year Kindelberger designed a basic trainer airplane which was accepted by the Army Air Corps in 1935. Then came other planes, including the P-51 Mustang fighter of World War II, and the B-25 Mitchell medium bomber. At the end of the war, North American was producing jets, and in 1946 it made its first study related to guided missiles. In 1948 the company began work on the Navaho missile with a study contract. Such success warranted expansion, and North American did expand. Soon it had two aircraft divisions, in Los Angeles and Columbus, Ohio, and an atomics international division, Rocketdyne, a missile development division, and one called Autonetics. Then, in 1957, the volatility of the defense and space businesses came home to North American—that year the Navaho program was canceled when Congress jibbed at the Defense Department's budgetary requests. North American suddenly lost a seventh of its business.

The company had assets, but it needed action. Its engineers were leaders in the design and production of liquid-propellant rocket engines, inertial guidance systems, and supersonic aerodynamics. But if work could not be found for them, these engineers would move on, like gypsies, to the companies which had secured the work.[2]

The 1958 North American went after two important NASA contracts; one of them was for the airframe of the Little Joe booster needed to put a man in space. That took care of one set of engineers and technicians who might other-

[2] North American Aviation Company history, pp. 1–7.

wise have been lost to the company. Rocketdyne division, which also was threatened by the loss of the Navaho, began to compete for the contract for the 1,500,000-pound thrust engine that NASA scientists and engineers would need in the future.

There were not, after all very many companies that conceivably could build so large a rocket engine. On October 21, 1958, NASA called together representatives of seven of these companies in Washington, to explain the space agency's problem.

(The following information is derived from Hearings before the Committee on Science and Astronautics of the United States House of Representatives, 86th Congress, Second Session, relative to the production of documents by NASA.)

The companies whose representatives appeared that day were: Aerojet General Corp.; Aircraft gas turbine division of General Electric Co.; Bell Aircraft Corp.; Pratt & Whitney aircraft division, United Aircraft Corp.; reaction motors division, Thiokol Chemical Corp.; Rocketdyne of North American; and Wright aeronautical division of Curtiss-Wright Corp. This represented generally the companies capable of undertaking such a program.

That conference was very general. Two days later, NASA sent a request for proposal to each of the seven firms, giving a statement of the technical requirements of the engine NASA wanted, and outlining the policies the government would follow in making facilities available and building new facilities. Those who were seriously interested must put in proposals by November 24. The provision for testing was extremely important in the companies' consideration of costs: the government indicated it would make available three test stands at Edwards Air Force Base, California, plus a control station; this meant that the successful contractor would not have to build expensive facilities, but he would have to include in his costs any money that would be needed to modify these structures. That presented a problem.

Of the seven firms, all but Bell Aircraft submitted proposals.

Wright aeronautical division proposed to build a liquid turborocket engine using a liquid oxygen/hydrocarbon propellant that would develop a thrust of a million pounds at sea level. The company would build a testing and engineering plant near Reno, Nevada, at a cost of $37,397,170; and a plant for the production of liquid oxygen that would cost an additional fifteen to eighteen million dollars. The company proposed that the government build the oxygen plant, and that government and company negotiate the other construction costs. This proposal did not completely comply with the NASA request, but Wright said it really did not have time to work out anything more definite.

Some parts of the engine would be built at the Curtiss-Wright plant in Wood Ridge, N.J., and then all would be moved to the western site. Altogether, the program would take forty-two months and the cost would be $75,509,987, plus another $11,474,830 for propellants used in testing. That came to $86,984,817, and Curtiss-Wright would like to receive a fixed fee of $5,285,699, which represented 7 per cent of the cost, outside the propellants. This did not include the facility cost of some fifty-two million dollars much of which obviously would have to be borne by the government. The total was $92,270,516-plus—and that was a very big plus.

Reaction Motors (which was the old American Rocket

Society Company) noted in its bid that it did not have adequate facilities to do the entire job. It would let subcontracts for parts to the Convair division of General Dyanmics and to Solar Aircraft Company, both at San Diego, and to Allison division of General Motors in Indianapolis. The Reaction Motors plant at Denville, N.J., would be used for design and making some small parts. Most tests would be made at Edwards Air Force Base. The company wanted the government to spend $12,734,081 for test equipment and facilities, a sum which was included in the company proposal, and another $9,917,307, a sum which was not. The total cost including these facilities, would be $179,674,474, and the company wanted a fixed fee of 9 per cent, or $16,170,692. Then would come cost of propellants and administrative expenses, with another 9 per cent fee, or $15,291,221 more. So the Reaction Motors proposal called for $211,136,387 and for very high fees based on many extra expenses to the government. No time span was indicated.

Pratt and Whitney proposed to build the rocket engine at plants in East Hartford, Connecticut, and West Palm Beach, Florida. Much of the testing would be done at Edwards Air Force Base. The program could take three and a half, four and a half, or five and a half years. For the longest program Pratt and Whitney wanted a $3,960,000-test stand built by the government at Edwards Air Force Base. For either of the shorter programs they wanted two 1,500,000-pound-thrust stands, which would cost $16 million. In both cases they wanted an additional $2,510,000 for test equipment and $6,777,000 for modification of existing Pratt and Whitney facilities. The company, however, would put up $7,940,000 for modification of some facilities and building new ones. Its fee would be 7 per cent. The total costs would be $61,972,321; $105,354,678; or $89,354,678, depending on what program was chosen.

General Electric offered a four-phase program, with work to be done at three GE plants, testing at a government station in New York and at Edwards Air Force Base. GE would not need any additional facilities, but there should be provision for $6,222,000 for modification of facilities, mostly government-owned. GE would furnish test equipment worth about three million dollars and office equipment worth one million dollars and negotiate amortization of this material. The fee would be 8 per cent of costs, and the total cost—said the company——would be $205,211,600. (Later the government discovered that the GE accountants had made an arithmetical error of $180,000 in their computations. Even the biggest of them make their mistakes!)

Aerojet General, the successor to the old von Karman company, proposed to build and test nearly all at the Aerojet plant in Sacramento, with final testing at Edwards Air Force Base. Aerojet wanted a new control station at Edwards (this was not included in the cost estimate). It wanted $5,360,358 for facilities modification and test equipment at the liquid rocket plant and $3,915,792 for facilities modification at Edwards. Aerojet also said it would put up $2,881,443 for facilities and equipment, and offered four programs, ranging from $105,490 to $143,319,210, with a fixed fee of 7 per cent.

Rocketdyne proposed to build the engine and test most of it at the company plants at Canoga Park, California, and in the Santa Susana mountains, ten miles away. Final tests would be performed at Edwards Air Force Base. Rocketdyne did not want any extra facilities built at Edwards, but asked for $8,529,424 for test equipment and facilities modification at the company plants to be used, and $170,200 for modification of government-owned facilities at these plants. Rocket-dyne's proposal was for $94,817,913, with a fee of 7.5 per cent.

The proposals ranged, then, from a $62 million, three-and-a-half-year proposal made by Pratt and Whitney to the $211 million plan submitted by Reaction Motors, and not one of them was completely comparable to another.

When the proposals came in they were first evaluated by a technical assessment team consisting of four representatives of NASA and three men from the Air Force—called in because they had been doing this kind of procurement for years. The team members met; they brought in technical consultants. Meanwhile a management team was meeting, too, to consider the proposals from the business point of view; on this team were six NASA men and two Air Force people.

The results of all these discussions and examinations were given to the five-man source selection board which represented NASA's management. Chief of the board was Dr. Abe Silverstein, director of space flight development for NASA. Members were J. W. Crowley, director of aeronautical and space research; Ralph Cushman, procurement and supply officer; A. Hyatt, assistant director for propulsion; and Robert G. Nunn, Jr., assistant general counsel.

The source evaluation board discussed the various proposals and made recommendations, individually, to administrator Glennan. On the basis of those recommendations, Glennan selected Rocketdyne's proposal; and on December 17, 1958, he wrote the Rocketdyne division to the effect that its proposal would be the basis for negotiations for the building of the rocket engine.

In the next few weeks, NASA had some changes of

heart and plan. The experts had been talking about a one-million-pound-thrust engine, but they decided they really wanted a 1,500,000-pound-thrust engine. Here was a problem typical of a research and development situation. The change in specifications could be the basis for an entire renegotiation of the bidding—but as time went on there would be so many changes in the contract that if this were the method of procedure nothing would ever get built.

When the negotiation was complete, the estimated cost had been raised by almost $1.5 million, and the percentage of Rocketdyne's fixed fee reduced to 6.5 per cent, or $6,254,-145.

One obvious reason for the selection of Rocketdyne was the familiarity of the Air Force men with the company's work. Rocketdyne, after all, had conducted one of the first and most effective studies of the big engine. Another was the fact that Rocketdyne was even then working closely with the Air Force, and certain needed materials could be furnished under existing contracts. Still another reason was the strong regard in Air Force and NASA circles for E. H. Kindelberger as a man who lived up to his commitments and did the job properly.

There were other reasons, of course. Some of them came out in testimony before a Congressional committee, when NASA made a statement on the selection. Rocketdyne's proposal was responsive to the request, the NASA men had confidence in the design, and they were pleased with the company's conservative approach to the technical problems. Rocketdyne's method of development would make it possible to test the thrust chamber early, and this was the key to the engine's performance. Not least was the admission that Rocketdyne's experience in the large liquid rocket engine field and its facilities and its engineering capabilities were "comparatively superior." So the maintenance of that large engineering staff after the dropout of the Navaho had been no mistake.

It was instructive to hear why the other companies were not selected. Aerojet General had offered a single design, a marginal cooling system, a revolutionary manner of cooling the combustion chamber, a bad system of timing of the tests, other technical ideas that were not acceptable. Finally, and most important, said NASA, "the company's experience, facilities, and technical capability were comparatively less favorable for the development of extraordinarily large liquid rocket engines."[3]

Pratt and Whitney's proposal was rejected because the company did not have the proper physical facilities, its cost estimates were unrealistic, its proposal was not detailed enough to give a basis for judgment. Finally, again, NASA decided this company lacked experience in the development of large rocket engines using liquid fuel.

Thiokol's Reaction Motors could scarcely be said to be a newcomer to the field, but its proposal failed, too. It was old-fashioned, the engine was too heavy, the timing of tests was not satisfactory, the cost estimate was highest of all, and "the physical facilities and technical capability of the company at the time were of doubtful adequacy without some facilities and personnel buildup."

Theirs was a story of failure. Reaction Motors was one of the early pioneers of rocketry, formed in 1942 by four members of the American Rocket Society. What had happened in the interim years? The company had simply let the technology go by them.

[3] NASA statement of reasons for selection of Rocketdyne proposal to General Accounting Office.

No one could fault General Electric on facilities and ability, yet its proposal failed, too. One reason given in the NASA report was that it was too far out—too radical. GE had suggested a design that was untried for big rockets, rendering the proposal what NASA called "high-risk." There was risk enough in the whole notion of man in space without asking for trouble with untried concepts.

Curtiss-Wright fell out because its proposal was technically not responsive, but probably more because the company suggested building a whole new plant and test facility near Reno, instead of using the existing facilities at Edwards Air Force Base.

No matter what else was apparent in these negotiations and in the award of the contract, one thing certainly stood out: them as had—got.

Bureaucracy

Almost concurrent with the negotiations to produce the big rocket, NASA found itself working out an even more complex problem: how to award a contract for a vehicle to put a man into space.

From the outset, North American had the edge in this negotiation. For who but North American had pioneered with the X-15, that experimental supersonic craft that was teaching the scientists and engineers so much about the mechanics of space flight?

Yet the awarding did not turn out to be that simple.

The beginnings of the manned flight spacecraft can be traced back to the meeting of January 29-31, 1958, at Wright Patterson Air Force Base, when McDonnell Aircraft Company, alone among some twenty companies, showed that it was thinking in the same direction that the NACA space engineers were. McDonnell offered a 2,400-pound ballistic missile type of space capsule that would be launched by an Atlas rocket with a Polaris in the second stage. North American, locked into the X-15 concept, proposed an extension of the X-15 idea, with a three-stage launch and the pilot eventually parachuting from the vehicle, which would be lost.

As the months wore on, Maxime Faget of NASA developed the concept of the ballistic capsule, and by spring it was fairly well agreed that his specifications would be its configuration. In April, Faget and Charles W. Mathews drafted preliminary specifications for the first manned satellite at Langley Aeronautical Laboratory. By this time General Electric had a study contract for manned space flight. And at the same time, McDonnell Aircraft was devoting its own money to a study that lasted eleven months.

In July, Republic Aviation sent men to Washington to impress the NASA staff with the work Republic had been doing on manned space flight. Republic still had the Ferri sled idea in mind, and had begun designing. The company made a fairly elaborate presentation, including discussion of a four-stage launch vehicle.

All this time, while NASA was being formed, various teams of engineers and scientists at the new agency's centers were being assigned the necessary studies for the manned space flight program. In September, the NASA space task group began studies of a tracking system. Other men worked on re-entry problems, life sciences, parachutes for the capsule, and the myriad other problems of the experiment. On November 7 a contractor briefing was held at Langley Research Center, and to this came some forty prospective bidders. After the discussion, about twenty of them dropped out, seeing that they did not have the capability for the project. But about twenty stayed in, and NASA began feeding these manufactures information.[1]

Specifications for the manned spacecraft were issued on November 14, and Republic was out of it—or at least the Ferri sled was out—for the Faget ballistic capsule was definitely to be the vehicle. Republic still indicated its intention of bidding, along with nineteen other firms, and a deadline of December 11, 1958, was set for submission of specific proposals.

On December 11 eleven firms submitted bids, and Winzen Research Laboratories submitted an incomplete proposal. The companies were:

Winzen Research Inc.	$ 4,601,612
Avco Manufacturing	12,595,368
Douglas Aircraft	12,919,969
Lockheed Aircraft	13,523,846
Republic Aviation	13,868,964
The Martin Company	13,914,844
Northrop Aircraft	14,731,810
Convair	17,203,424
Chance-Vought Aircraft	17,272,296
McDonnell Aircraft	17,583,917
Grumman Aircraft	27,336,330
North American Aviation	35,169,399

[1] The above and much of the following comes from *Project Mercury, A Chronology*, prepared by NASA, 1963.

A very, very careful assessment of these proposals began. Eleven technical teams evaluated the eleven different bids. These assessments were sent up to a technical assessment committee. A management committee examined the proposals from the standpoint of cost, management, and production. The technical committee had finished its work and reported on December 30 to the source selection board. The management committee reported on January 6. The source selection board met three times, and made its recommendation to the administrator. On January 9, Dr. Glennan gave the contract to McDonnell Aircraft Co.

On the face of it, McDonnell seemed one of the most unlikely candidates. Its bid was far from low—only two bids were higher. Of the firms competing it might have seemed that Avco, General Electric, and North American were more experienced in capsule design and could do a better job. But the matter was not that simple, for McDonnell had played its cards extremely well. In the first place, the company had gotten off to a good start by coming up in January with ideas for what the NACA experts were thinking about—a ballistic capsule. Then McDonnell had hurried to put together its own study program, at its own expense (although that is a relative matter, since the money obviously came out of research and development funds relegated from other government contracts). McDonnell had also taken the trouble to keep track of the NASA experts' changes in thinking, as any of the other companies might have done. But not all had. North American and General Electric, both of which had held study contracts and built full-scale mockups of space cabins, with crew provision, pushed themselves out of the running by offering proposals in which the designed capsule would be too heavy for insertion into orbit by an Atlas ICBM alone.[2]

McDonnell was selected for a number of reasons. First of all, the McDonnell technical proposal was deemed to be excellent by the technical advisors to NASA. The whole adventure was going to be very risky. McDonnell had arrived at its plan using simple, reliable, tested concepts of design, and systems integration that had worked before under different circumstances; this configuration appealed to the NASA men. The whole concept of manned space flight left so many imponderables that they were grateful for the integration of proven concepts.

Second, McDonnell proposed using materials that had been tested and structures that had been tried out earlier and found to work. Where the company did come up with a novel plan, as in the escape system, its engineers had made a thorough documentation and presented convincing arguments for their ideas. (The results of the eleven-month company study program obviously showed here.)

One of the big unknowns was the re-entry and landing question. Here McDonnell's engineers made careful and complete statements, sticking again to developed equipment where it could be used, and arguing convincingly for new items. In attitude control, for example, the manual and automatic systems were entirely independent of one another—an important safety factor. For the environmental control systems, McDonnell had worked out cabin pressures, temperature regulation, atmospheric composition, re-

[2] Letter from James P. Gleason, assistant administrator NASA, to Raymond Wilcove, staff consultant, House of Representatives Committee on Science and Astronautics, August 19, 1959.

moval of waste products, nutrition of the astronauts, and survival equipment.

Technically, then, the McDonnell program was superior to most of the others; it was more complete; it fitted the concepts developed by the space task group.

One other company, Grumman, had also submitted a complete and resourceful technical proposal. Like McDonnell, the Grumman engineers had considered controls, navigation aids, the communication system, and the power system for the capsule, and had arrived at convincing answers. Several of the other firms had presented only partial programs, or had shown themselves to be off base in at least one element the NASA task group considered vital. One proposal indicated that the engineers were on doubtful ground in their aerodynamic design. Another showed little concern for the relationship between design and fabrication of the equipment. (In other words, it looked pretty, but how in the world would you build it?) One proposal called for an escape system that might destroy the capsule without first effecting the escape of the pilot. Several of the proposals were so unrealistic in their approach to re-entry and landing that the NASA task force doubted they would bring back the astronaut at all. One did not provide for any independent attitude control system (automatic or manual). Several adopted radical approaches to the environmental control system—and, as noted, NASA did not favor unnecessarily radical approaches to known problems when there were so many unknowns in which all approaches must be deemed radical until they could be proved. Where most of the contractors made a vital error was in offering unusual departures without enough supporting evidence to make a convincing case:

> *Several proposals omitted some necessary designs, a deficiency frequently associated with poor engineering choices for the solution of some specific problem. Finally, some presentations were very general and promised merely to meet the specifications without sufficient discussions as to how the specifications would be met; and, in the other direction, other presentations were overly complex and appeared unreliable for use in the Mercury vehicle.*[3]

In proposals for management, four companies were regarded as strongest, but when management and technical aspects were combined, as they had to be, the choice narrowed down to Grumman and McDonnell. And then came another very important consideration in terms of policy, politics, and general economics. Grumman had many new Navy projects in hand, several of them in the beginning stages. There was question whether Grumman could do its Navy work properly and still take on the Mercury project. Administrator Glennan considered, and decided that it would be wiser to take McDonnell.

In mid-January 1959, several representatives of NASA traveled to St. Louis to visit the McDonnell plant and study the facilities available for the job. They began working up a contract, and in the course of the negotiations the McDonnell estimate rose from $17,583,917 to $18,300,000, largely because of changes that NASA wanted in the design. McDonnell wanted this contract badly enough that it had agreed to negotiate its fee. When the time came, the company asked for a fixed fee of 7 per cent of the reimbursable

[3] Statement of the administrator of NASA on the selection of McDonnell Aircraft Corp. to design and construct a manned satellite capsule, project Mercury, part of the House subcommittee hearings on the production of documents by NASA, January 27 and 29, 1960, Committee on Science and Astronautics.

cost, and the fee was actually negotiated at 6.28 per cent.[4]

By the spring of 1959, Representative Overton Brooks, chairman of the House of Representatives Committee on Science and Astronautics, had become very much interested in the Rocketdyne and McDonnell contracts. There was talk around Washington that the low bidder had not been selected in either case—indeed, that in the McDonnell case the bidder was one of the very highest. In general, Congressmen were suspicious of such practice, and Brooks and his committee undertook to discover just what had happened in these two important contracts that the new agency had let.

Brooks wrote to Glennan, asking for a copy of the contract, the specifications of NASA, a memo on the early briefing, the bidders' proposals, and the reports of the technical and management teams. Finally Brooks wanted the report of the source selection board which had advised Dr. Glennan on the matter.

The committee recognized the problems inherent in discussion of this material, Brooks said. Anything that was classified or contained trade secrets of the industry would be handled very carefully. The committee did not even need to receive such material, but would send representatives to NASA to look it over.

On June 15, Glennan replied. He sent over the contract and the specifications. There was no memorandum of the first bidders' conference, but he included a list of names of the participants, who could be brought to question. As to the contractors' proposals, Glennan was willing to let

4 Letter of Frank H. Wetzel, assistant comptroller general of the United States, to Rep. Overton Brooks, January 14, 1960 (part of the House Committee hearings on the production of documents).

the representatives of the committee see them, but was very cautious about protecting NASA's relations with business firms. "Contractors' proposals are treated by NASA as confidential business matters," he wrote. The technical team and management team reports did not exist, because the teams had reported verbally to the source selection board.

As to the final report, that of the source selection board, Glennan would not release it. The reason: it represented the personal judgments of subordinate members of the NASA staff, made confidentially to the administrator to help him make his decision. He was protecting his subordinates.

Representative Brooks and his committee did not agree with Glennan's point of view. They believed it was more in the public interest to have full disclosure of the information than protection of subordinates. The day following the date of Glennan's letter, Brooks wrote to Joseph Campbell, comptroller general of the United States, and asked for an investigation of the bids and contract. Campbell asked Glennan for the source selection board report, too.

Again Glennan refused. This time he cited the Constitutional question of the privilege of the executive to withhold documents from the legislative branch, or even from other branches of the executive. Glennan took full responsibility for the selection of North American.

His answer satisfied neither the General Accounting Office nor the Congressional committee. The committee decided to go further into NASA activities and probe the McDonnell contract, and on July 9 a staff member asked NASA for the same kind of information that had been requested about the Rocketdyne contract—including the report of the source selection board. Glennan's answer was predictably the same as before. No.

Brooks's response was to urge the General Accounting

Office to get the reports. The committee would undertake a continuing study of NASA, the Bureau of Standards, and the National Science Foundation, he said. "These are the agencies over which this committee has legislative jurisdiction and it will henceforth be the policy of this committee to scrutinize the contracts entered into by these agencies in space development and in scientific research and development."

These, of course, were warning words.

During the summer and fall of 1959 the General Accounting Office made several attempts to secure the vital source selection board reports, but Glennan would not be moved. By January 1960, the committee considered public hearings on the question, for by this time the matter had been taken by Glennan to the White House, and he was backed in his position by President Eisenhower, if not directly, then indirectly, in the manner Eisenhower liked to affect, through his staff.

The General Accounting Office took a dim view of the withholding of these documents. Comptroller Campbell reported to the Brooks committee that the Glennan action was unwarranted because it prevented the accounting office from satisfying the request of the committee for information, and also it was "a direct interference with our statutory responsibilities."

The expressed concern was that NASA, an untried agency, would spend billions of dollars of the taxpayers' money in the future. "The precedent set here," said Campbell, "unless changed, means that many millions of dollars will be spent in a manner that cannot be adequately reviewed."[5]

Brooks and his committee felt that NASA was violating

[5] Brooks committee hearings report, p. 133.

the letter and spirit of the law which had established the agency. In consideration of the NASA bill, Representative McCormick of the committee had raised the specific point that the administrator of NASA be *directed* to make public disclosure of what the administration was doing. Here, in the committee's view, was another case of the executive seizing powers that did not belong to it, and undermining the power of Congress.[6]

In the hearings that began on January 27, 1960, Robert F. Keller, general counsel, stated the case for the General Accounting Office:

> *The nonavailability of the reports of the chairman of the source selection board and other documents, means that the sole documentary links between the opinions of important segments of NASA necessary for proper evaluation of the proposals and the final decisions to select the Rocketdyne and McDonnell proposals are missing. Without these key documents there is no positive evidence that the findings of the technical and management teams were relied upon, accepted in part, or rejected altogether.*[7]

In the interim—between the time that the argument began and the hearings occurred—another contract was awarded for boosters for the Little Joe launch vehicle. Since this contract called for expenditures below a million dollars, the decision was made at a level lower than that of the administrator. All the details of the contracting, including the reports of the technical and management people, were made available to Congress. Keller suggested that this action represented inconsistency. The point was: were small

6 Brooks committee report, pp. 34–35.
7 *Ibid.*, p. 4.

contracts to be carefully scrutinized while the large and important ones were kept secret?

In the interim, too, President Eisenhower had been called upon for other reasons to make a statement of policy regarding the matter of executive privilege, and he had come out flatly for the protection of the confidential relationship between subordinates of executive departments and the department heads.

Glennan went so far as to tell the committee in general terms that the source selection boards in both the Rocketdyne and McDonnell cases had approved these contract awards. ("I haven't gone against the advice of any of my selection boards yet.") But he remained firm on the matter of the principle.

The hearings ended inconclusively, with the committee expressing its hope that NASA would be more cooperative in the future.

By this time NASA was thoroughly aroused to the danger it was in from Congressional disapproval, unless it could substantiate the position that Glennan had taken as consistent with other government operations. At Glennan's request, McKinsey & Company's consultant John Corson suggested on January 26 an independent investigation of major NASA contracts to be carried out by a committee organized by NASA. The contracts to be checked were the North American Rocketdyne contract for the big engine, the Chance-Vought contract for the Scout test vehicle, the McDonnell contract for the Mercury capsule, the Western Electric contract for Mercury tracking, the Convair contract for the Vega program, and a contract with Linde Air Products Company to produce liquid oxygen.

There were other problems to be considered at this

time. In NASA's first sixteen months its staff had grown from nine thousand people to sixteen thousand; the annual budget had trebled to a billion dollars; the agency was struggling to absorb the Jet Propulsion Laboratory and the von Braun team, and was expanding in every direction.

So a blue-ribbon committee was organized, to investigate NASA's organization. Known as the Kimpton committee, it was headed by Lawrence Kimpton, chancellor of the University of Chicago. Other members were Elmer Lindseth, president of the Cleveland Electric and Illuminating Company; Morehead Patterson, chairman of American Machine and Foundry; Nathan W. Pearson, vice-president of T. Mellon and Sons; Dr. James A. Perkins, vice-president of the Carnegie Corporation of New York; Charles Stauffacher, executive vice-president of Continental Can Company; and Fletcher Waller, vice-president of Bell & Howell.

The Kimpton committee was basically organized and staffed by McKinsey & Company. At the same time Corson secured a $65,000 contract with NASA to study the agency's contracting and industrial relationships. The two studies proceeded simultaneously and, as NASA historian Rosholt put it, "The work of McKinsey & Co. preparing the report on NASA contracting and giving staff assistance to the Kimpton committee became so intertwined that there is a considerable amount of overlap between the Contracting Report and the Kimpton Report."

In the autumn of 1960 both were in process. The McKinsey study was one hundred pages long. To cut down business competition and speed the effort, it recommended that NASA farm out 70 to 85 per cent of its space flight experiments to universities and other elements of the scientific community. NASA should also plan to contract with industry for some space vehicles. NASA should be decentralized, with total responsibility for a project placed at one NASA center; and each project should be managed by a team of managers and technicians, headed by a project manager. There were also criticisms and suggestions for bettering NASA's procurement system and its buying, and some toughening of the NASA contract negotiation procedures. NASA took these recommendations to heart. Indeed, during the study a contract negotiator named W. William Quintrell made serious objections to the McKinsey contract. He asked that the professional fees of each of the McKinsey personnel involved in these studies be stated so that NASA could evaluate the contract. McKinsey & Company said this was not its policy. But Quintrell continued to bore in, and before he was finished he showed how well NASA was learning its lessons about contracting with industry—by reducing the McKinsey contract by $1,125.

Meanwhile John Corson and the McKinsey staff were touring NASA installations with the Kimpton committee, and helping draft the report for that group of busy businessmen.

As with any committee, progress was slow. For example, one day someone took a tape recorder into the room where Corson was meeting with the committee members to work out the report:[8]

VOICE: A transmittal letter will have to be adapted now as we talk about it.
VOICE: Can I read this?
VOICE: I have copies of it here.
    [A document was read into the record.]
VOICE: That is the title of what is included on the first page.

[8] Undated transcript of meeting in files of NASA Historical section.

VOICE: The conclusions and recommendations contained in this report are based on [unintelligible]:

Two, a series of many meetings from April 15 to September 30 of this year . . . at NASA headquarters, Washington, D.C., Washington Space Flight Center, Langley, Patrick Air Force Base. . . .

Three, interviews with officials of the Executive Office of the President, Department of Defense, Department of State, . . .

VOICE: Did we number the interviews?

VOICE: I think it is rather impressive.

VOICE: The total of approximately X interviews.

VOICE: Also the Bureau of the Budget, I think we ought to be quite specific.

VOICE: Did you ever follow up that lecture . . .?

VOICE: I have been in touch with him a number of times. When you say follow up—

VOICE: The memoranda they gave us. Did you ever discuss those?

VOICE: My impression was that they were dealing with a different level of either detail or concept, that they were talking about . . . and that we didn't really have to come back with any rejoinder.

VOICE: I didn't think so either. I really think they were more tentative than our statement even implies. These were preliminary thoughts and if you went there today they might have some second thoughts.

VOICE: I suggest in Point Three that the interviews with blank or X number of officials with the Department of Defense and Department of State, University Centers, plus Director of the Bureau of the Budget, the Chief, Science Advisory Projects. . . .

VOICE: The suggestion that the detail be given of the people we have interviewed—

VOICE: At least in terms of numbers of interviews, and identify them.

VOICE: Four: Interviews with scores of NASA officials, including the administrator, deputy administrator, and associate administrator, representatives of the six headquarters, technical and administrative offifices, the three space flight centers and three advanced research centers—

VOICE: The score bothers me.

VOICE: The advisory committee takes this opportunity to express its appreciation to the administrator and the entire NASA organization for the genuine cooperation and assistance—

VOICE: Here are a couple of words: candor and courtesy; for the genuine cooperation, candor, and courtesy.

VOICE: That is good literary style. This really takes a bite.

VOICE: That is Ray's program.

VOICE: I am sorry that one is on the record.

VOICE: The staff of McKinsey and Company, Inc., for the preparation of working papers—

VOICE: I would like to suggest on this final report, I would like to eliminate that. I would like to eliminate this because, A, I think from your standpoint the report ought to be more your document. The work papers we did prepare in a different sense. You didn't go over them paragraph by paragraph in the same way. Does this make sense?

VOICE: We shouldn't have been given credit for the final report. It is the . . . committee's report. I think maybe a phrase— and continuing assistance throughout our meeting and interviews or something of this sort.

VOICE: How about the preparation of work papers and staff assistance?

VOICE: Just staff assistance.

VOICE: Would that suffice?

VOICE: I think this is hopelessly unsatisfactory without my name.

VOICE: No, look, John, hush.

VOICE: I think the staff of McKinsey and Company . . .

VOICE: Something like that . . .

VOICE: Only a little more flowery phrase . . .

VOICE: John Corson and his staff of McKinsey and Company . . .

VOICE: I agree.

VOICE: If there is any part of this that anybody objects to, I want everybody cleared.

VOICE: Couldn't we say Mr. John Corson and his staff?

VOICE: I have no particular objections but I also have no desire to have it in here, either.

VOICE: If there is no company policy . . .

VOICE: Do you want to qualify the "excellent" staff of McKinsey and Company?

VOICE: Certainly.

VOICE: I like that a lot better.

VOICE: We might as well give them a plug.

VOICE: I would like to ask two questions about this letter, if I may.

Is there anything now that you have overlooked in the letter? I don't know that there is. Shouldn't we ask ourselves is there anything else that we ought to say in this letter? I am inclined to think not.

VOICE: We can make a postscript.

VOICE: There is no necessary connection between the resignation of Mr. Kimpton of the University of Chicago and his assumption of . . . [Kimpton had resigned from the university and was about to take a job with Standard Oil Company]

VOICE: If I were writing it myself, seriously, I would make the paragraph about NASA a separate paragraph. I think we should express some appreciation to the administrator and the entire oragnization of NASA for the genuine cooperation, candor, and courtesy during the course of our study period. We also wish to acknowledge the assistance and preparation in the committee's work of the excellent staff of McKinsey & Company and of Mr. Corson . . .

VOICE: I agree . . .

And so it went, until finally the committee completed its report, a report that basically assured the status quo. But that suddenly became relatively unimportant, for it was the autumn of 1960, an election year.

9

Some Politics and the Big Change

Congress and the nation at large were not very happy with the American space program by the middle of 1960. Some Congressmen and some publicists had indicated that American prestige was riding on the space program, a contention President Eisenhower denied. But the Mercury program was not going very well. The McDonnell contract, it was now estimated, would turn out to cost $119 million rather than the original $19,450,000, because—it was said—the original figure had been nothing more than an estimate of the minimum necessary to get the program started. A dozen more space vehicles had been ordered by NASA in the months just past, and there had been considerable increases in the cost of nearly every item over the estimates laid down in the beginning. What this all said, in essence, was that the original contract specifications were meaningless, and what McDonnell was now going to do had very little relationship to the basis on which the contract was awarded. This problem, however, was typical in the research and development field. Not having ever done it before, no one knew precisely how to put a man into space, so there was bound to be a good deal of guesswork and some bad estimating.

By midsummer, McDonnell's first spacecraft suitable for manned flight was on the launch pad at Cape Canaveral. It was to be launched unmanned to show the capability of the Mercury capsule to carry a man in actual space flight. It was to fly for sixteen minutes, achieve an altitude of 98 nautical miles over a range of 1,300 nautical miles, and be recovered.

This spacecraft (No. 4) was launched on an Atlas ICBM. One minute after liftoff all contact was lost. The mission was a total failure, and nobody really knew what had happened.

The vehicle had exploded, an investigating committee discovered. So it was back to the drawing boards, and the manned spaceflight program was delayed for six months while the engineers worked out their problems.[1]

Space was very much on the public mind that summer and fall. The Russians put animals (dogs, mice, rats, flies, etc.) into orbit and recovered them successfully. The Air Force put various kinds of hardware into orbit and recovered some of it. For America, however, the most significant

[1] *This New Ocean*, pp. 271–79.

feat was the successful launch of Echo I, an inflated ten-story balloon.

The inception of the Echo project is usually credited to Arthur C. Clarke, the English scientist and science fiction writer, who in 1945 wrote a visionary article for the magazine *Wireless World* about a manned satellite in space that would relay television signals between continents.[2]

In January 1946, at Fort Monmouth, New Jersey, the Army Signal Corps proved that it was possible to bounce microwave radar signals off the moon and back. This discovery started scientists to thinking of practical applications, and in November 1954, Dr. John R. Pierce of Bell Telephone Laboratories delivered a paper at Princeton University advocating a space satellite communications system. Then, on December 18, 1958, the Air Force launched Score, a satellite with a tape recorder that transmitted messages (some were Christmas greetings) from space for twelve days before its batteries ran down.

For obvious reasons, the Bell Telephone Company was intrigued by the idea of bouncing signals around the world, and in 1959 it bounced signals from laboratories at Holmdel, New Jersey, off the moon, and then to the Jet Propulsion Laboratory in Goldstone, California.

Although radio transmissions curve, television transmissions travel in a straight line and thus cannot be shot around the earth. But by using a satellite, shooting a transmission from one point on earth to a satellite along a straight line above and then off the satellite to another earth point at another angle, the same result as curved transmission can be achieved.

[2] *The Bell System's Role in Satellite Communications,* published by the Bell System.

The Bell System proposed a joint undertaking with NASA to study long-range communications using an orbiting earth satellite. Bell Laboratories had already done much of the spadework in the preparation of the satellite. A horn-reflector antenna was set up to catch the microwave reflections from Echo. Tracking stations were built to track the satellite by radar, electronic computers, and telescope.

At Cape Canaveral on August 12, 1960, a Thor-Delta missile was launched, carrying the folded balloon, and 1,000 miles up the balloon was put onto a circular orbit about the earth at 16,000 miles per hour. In the days to come two-way telephone conversations were held between New Jersey and California, using the balloon as a relay station, and signals were transmitted to Europe as well. The feasibility of a communications satellite system had been proved, and it was to become an important part of the space business.

That summer of 1960, even as project Mercury was working to put a man into space, NASA was planning project Apollo, which would put three men into orbit in a much larger spacecraft. But the failures continued apace. Congressman Brooks was very pointedly dissatisfied with the progress of the Mercury program. The whole space effort became a political affair in the presidential campaign. On election day (November 8), a new firing of the space capsule was tried, along with the Little Joe booster rocket system. It failed; the three components stuck together and crashed. On November 21 there was another failure, as the Redstone rocket lifted approximately four inches, and then the Rocketdyne A-7 engine cut out. This represented the absolute nadir of morale among the men working on project Mercury.[3]

The Russians, at the same time, were boasting that they

[3] *This New Ocean*, p. 293.

were on the threshold of achieving manned space flight. Early in December they put two more dogs into orbit, and then tried to bring them back. The system failed and the dogs died, but the Russians seemed very sanguine about it all, and the result was a very definite feeling of worry in America, where the space race was being taken seriously.

As 1960 ended, the American space program was very much in doubt in just about every department. Congress, and particularly the committees that dealt with the space effort, was chagrined at the slow progress. Newspaper and magazine writers were taking very negative views of the administration of the space program. President Eisenhower said many times that the United States was not in a race with the Russians, but practically nobody else felt that way about it.

After the election, the armed forces hoped to regain some of the ground they had lost in the space business, because as a candidate John F. Kennedy had linked space and defense in his "missile-gap" attacks on the Eisenhower Administration. The Air Force and the Navy both spoke of extending their space activities.

Instead, President Kennedy appointed a new committee to study the space problem and recommend an American posture. Dr. Jerome Wiesner of Massachusetts Institute of Technology was appointed chairman, and he had eight other prominent Americans to assist him. A few days after the first of the year the committee reported to the President-elect.

The Wiesner report was very critical of the Eisenhower space plan. The committee suggested five motivations for a vigorous space program, leading with national prestige— the aspect that Eisenhower had considered to be relatively unimportant. National security was the second reason, not the first, and the interests of pure science were third. Then came "practical nonmilitary application" or what might be termed the spin-off part of the space business. Finally the committee mentioned possibilities for international cooperation.[4]

The Wiesner report was very tough, blaming NASA management (and by inference the Eisenhower Administration) for underfulfilling all aspects of the space program. It paid some obeisance to achievement in the scientific area, but even here, it said, more could have been done if the application had been more thorough. The trouble was the leadership and the organization.

So what was being said in 1960 and 1961 was that the McKinsey plans and the Kimpton program were really quite insufficient.

Hindsight has always dogged the space program, for it is fairly simple to examine the deficiencies of the space agency a few months after this failure or that one. But the new administration was really talking about a basic change in the placement of the space program within the list of national objectives. It was to be given a very high priority.

One specific criticism was that NASA was devoting too much time, effort, and money to the development of "in-house" research. The Kimptom committee had recommended its removal, but within NASA many leading officials felt that the agency needed to keep control of more programs by actually operating research and development in the NASA facilities. Perhaps this was a carry-over from the old NACA philosophy, where the practice was a reasonable one. For the aeronautics committee was, after all, a small

4 Rosholt, p. 186.

research-oriented agency devoted to furthering the aeronautical sciences and dedicated to assistance of the Army, Navy, Air Force, and civil aviation. It had been normal for NACA to regard its own work as paramount. But in 1958 NACA had been transformed into something entirely different in principle. And subsequently the priorities changed steadily, until by 1961 what was wanted from NASA was an immensely capable supervisory agency that could bring together diverse elements in American industry to accomplish a "crash" program yet with such deliberate speed that there would be no mistakes. At this time the American political system provided NASA and the space program an excellent form of assistance: the coming of a new and politically opposite administration meant that change was inevitable. Without disgrace or any negative charges Glennan was expected and expecting to step down. What would be important was the nature and extent of the change in administration and orientation of the space agency.

Dr. Wiesner and his committee had recommended a technically oriented organization, the establishment of a "vigorous, imaginative, and *technically competent* top management."[5]

The politicians, however, did not entirely agree with the scientists and technicians. In this matter, President Kennedy had the active counsel of Vice President Lyndon Johnson, who carried much authority, for he had studied space and defense matters thoroughly in his long tenure in the Senate. Lyndon Johnson wanted a strong administrator, whatever else his qualifications might be, to run the space agency. The scientific advisers around Kennedy wanted a strong scientific management. In the compromise that was

5 Rosholt, p. 186.

effected, James Webb, a businessman, was selected to be administrator of NASA; the scientists were appeased by the appointment of Hugh L. Dryden to remain as deputy administrator.

James E. Webb was a remarkable man who, it could be said, was almost trained for the job. He was sixty years old at the time of the appointment, but had a vigor undiminished by the years. He had been educated as a teacher and lawyer, but he was also a Marine Corps reserve officer and a man well versed in government and the aeronautical and space business. For seven years he had been with a company dealing in technologies—Sperry Gyroscope. There he was personnel director, secretary and treasurer, and vice president, successively—which meant he dealt with the problems of this engineering and scientific business on many levels. He had been Under Secretary of the Treasury and Director of the Bureau of the Budget—which thoroughly acquainted him with the hard-eyed view of government management. He had been Under Secretary of State—which made him familiar with public policymaking at the highest levels.

One of Webb's particular fields of interest and competence was the interrelationships among science—including scientific education and applied science—business, and government. While living in Oklahoma City in the 1950's, he had been extremely active in arousing citizen interest in the sciences. He had been chairman of the southwest seminars in public responsibility at the University of Oklahoma and a trustee of the Frontiers of Science Foundation there. He had done much to bring an atomic-age attitude to Oklahoma and to southwestern education.

In business, he had long been associated with technological concerns: Kerr-McGee Oil Industries, which range
far and wide; Republic Supply Company; and finally McDonnell Aircraft Co. of St. Louis, which had recently secured
the contract to manufacture the Mercury space capsule.[6]
Obviously, as a director of McDonnell, James Webb was
familiar with the space business. A condition of appointment, of course, was that he sever his relations with McDonnell and others who did business with NASA, but it was
recognized by Congress that here was a man perhaps
uniquely qualified to manage the space agency. It was not
at all harmful, either, that he was a particular friend of the
late Senator Robert Kerr of Oklahoma and was highly regarded by Vice President Johnson.

Webb was criticized as a nonscientist by those who
hoped the time had come for scientists to take over administration of programs such as NASA. He was also criticized
because of his close association with the Senatorial "club"
in which Senator Kerr was a prime mover. But his nomina-
tion came before the Senate Committee on Aeronautical
and Space Sciences, to which Senator Kerr had succeeded
Lyndon Johnson as chairman. The Senate was enthusiastic
over the appointment.[7] It came at a time of crisis in NASA's
affairs, when many scientists thought the manned program
ought to be scrapped in favor of the more scientific unmanned programs that were showing greater signs of success. The military, seeing NASA weakening in the fall of
1960, had begun pressing to recreate strong military space
programs at the space agency's expense. If there were ever

[6] NASA authorization 1966, pp. 4–5.
[7] *This New Ocean*, pp. 307–308.

to be a time when NASA might stand or fall on the skills of its administrator, the beginning of 1961 was that time. Hardly had Webb sat down behind the desk at NASA head-quarters when, on April 12, came the word that the U.S.S.R. had successfully put a man (Yuri Gagarin) into orbit around the earth and recovered him without injury.

Immediately, all the old objections against manned space flight programs were submerged. The House Committee on Science and Astronautics began hearings within forty-eight hours of the news. The Administration began its own study of the manned flight program. NASA, of course, was proceeding with project Mercury. In January, James Webb had made recommendations for more emphasis (and money) for the program, but the Bureau of the Budget had trimmed them down so that there had been no acceleration. Early in 1960 Maxime Faget was working out designs for a space capsule to carry three men. It did not have a name nor did the concept. Unfortunately the day chosen by NASA to announce the Apollo project, which would follow Mercury, was the day the Mercury-Atlas 1 exploded just after liftoff, and that did not help matters a bit. When budgeting time came around at the end of 1960, the manned space program was held down by the Bureau of the Budget.

All that changed with the Gagarin flight. The Kennedy Administration suddenly became vitally concerned with the "space race." On May 25, 1961, President Kennedy gave a State of the Union Message to a joint session of Congress, and the burden of it was to announce that America would move forward to take leadership in the space race if it could. He called on Congress and the nation to back an expanded space program, with emphasis on a landing on the moon within the decade.

NASA's budget was to be increased by 61 per cent, and NASA's ten-year plan had to be drastically changed. NASA had become the eighth-largest federal agency in terms of its budget. The space business had become big business.

The Lunar Contractors and Other Constellations

James Webb set out to bring strong management to NASA. He began the program in the difficult days of 1961, as the Mercury project seemed to be faltering, Congress was watching with unconcealed disapproval and the Russians were forging ahead. As President Kennedy prepared his plan for an expanded space program, Webb was making the agency tight enough in management to carry the program out. It was a fortuitous combination.

One of the important changes in the agency was to prepare for the new projected moon-landing deadline of 1969.

Business would have to do most of the work, but there had to be a new kind of control.[1]

More than two years earlier the Space Task Group had been formed at NASA, and as time had gone along, this force came to have a kind of life of its own. It was basically concerned with the problems of putting man into orbit in space. In 1960 the group had expanded, and was suffering seriously from lack of coordination and facilities. Officially it was located at the Langley Research Center in Virginia, but it had outgrown its quarters. One of James Webb's first actions was to ask for the money to build a special manned space flight center. The Bureau of the Budget stiffly cut this from the request in the first go around, but after the Kennedy State of the Union address the appropriation went through, for $28 million.

Immediately there was competition for the selection of the new site, and a site survey team was sent out to examine the possibilities. The people around Langley were particularly eager to have the facility, but so were a half dozen other communities, and as usual political and economic considerations came into play. The area around Houston, Texas, was finally chosen for the Manned Spacecraft Center. A one-thousand-acre tract of land on Clear Lake, an inlet of Galveston Bay, would be given the government by Rice University.

The considerations had been availability of educational institutions in the area, electric power in abundance, water supply, climate, housing, water and air transportation, and recreational facilities. If other communities could sniff at the dripping Houston climate and wonder about the air facilities, and compare their own educational, industrial, and

1 Rosholt, pp. 202 *et seq.*

recreational facilities favorably, well, they did not have the political "muscle" at the moment. Vice President Lyndon B. Johnson was chairman of the National Aeronautics and Space Council, which Kennedy had rejuvenated. Representative Albert Thomas of Houston was a very important man on the House Appropriations Committee. Administrator Webb said that the decision was made in view of administrative factors: the expansion of the facilities at Cape Canaveral, and the building of a space vehicle plant near New Orleans. If that were solely the case, all these facilities might well have been placed somewhere in the hinterland of Florida. But it has always been an American practice to split up the pork from the barrel; the Air Force Academy had gone to Colorado Springs partly to spread around the gravy. The Houston site certainly would do as well as many another.

Construction began late in 1961, and the next year the Space Task Group moved into temporary location in Houston. Soon eighty thousand acres of land on Merritt Island in Florida (next to the Air Force test range) were purchased, its orange groves allowed to go into disarray while the houses and outbuildings were converted to warehouses. So the center of the space business moved to the southeast.

The manned space flight program had now become very complicated. The Mercury project, in terms of flights, was just beginning, but two succeeding programs were already in the works. One was project Gemini, which would involve a two-man space capsule to be put in orbit around the earth for a comparatively long period of time.[2] The other was project Apollo.

Project Mercury was designed to get a man into orbit. As early as 1959 NASA officials were talking about a second

[2] Project Gemini chronology.

phase that would include putting two craft into orbit and making a rendezvous between them. That year McDonnell, the prime contractor for the Mercury project, made a study of the problems outlined and presented a three hundred-page report on its findings. Here was a very sensible business gesture, to encourage the extension of the Mercury contract into a new field.

The report was well received and the Space Task Group was so impressed that it undertook serious consideration of the proposals. A good part of the business battle was thus won.

In February 1961, NASA officials began discussions with McDonnell men for an advanced Mercury spacecraft. Maxime Faget talked to McDonnell vice president Walter F. Burke about a two-man capsule on the same order, and Burke ordered a design to be made. The McDonnell project team for Mercury numbered some thirty to forty engineers, but now more were added, as the Space Task Group authorized $2,500,000 for the project. Soon NASA headquarters was talking in terms of a billion-dollar program—and Congress was listening because this was May 1961, just after Gagarin's flight.[3]

The Martin Company, builders of the Titan II missile, wanted NASA to use that launch vehicle, and a study was begun. Three study contracts of $100,000 each were let to Goodyear Aircraft Co., North American Aviation, and Ryan Aircraft Company for development of a paraglider program to bring the new space vehicle back to earth safely. In October, McDonnell secured a letter extension of its Mercury contract, and Martin persuaded NASA to take on Titan II at a cost of about $47.5 million.

[3] *Ibid.*, pp. 6–7.

The McDonnell contract was a "sole-source" contract, which provided for costs plus a fixed fee. NASA declared that McDonnell was the only firm capable of doing what was wanted by NASA in reasonable time and at reasonable cost—and since the Gemini vehicle was to be very much a modification of the Mercury, this argument carried much weight. As to the launch vehicles, NASA would get these through the Air Force. This was now October 1961, and the actual flights of Gemini were to be a dozen in number, running from the spring of 1963 to spring 1965. In December, the Martin Company received the order from the Air Force for fifteen Gemini launch vehicles and the necessary ground equipment to put them up.

In July that year, as the Mercury project was actually in the mission stage, and the Gemini program was in the contract and design stage, NASA accelerated its activities in response to President Kennedy's timetable of a man on the moon before 1970. In July, then, NASA conducted an industry conference dedicated to discussion of the project of putting a man on the moon—the Apollo project. Some three hundred companies were in attendance, sending twelve hundred representatives to the meeting. NASA officials and engineers spoke and were on hand to discuss what industry would be called upon to undertake this program.

James Webb later evaluated what the central problem was:[4]

> *To do this kind of advanced aeronautical and space research and build flight hardware, American industry has had to introduce new, very difficult fabrication and test capabilities. It has had to learn to use new management systems.*

[4] Hearings before the Committee on Aeronautical and Space Sciences, United States Senate, May 19, 1967 (Apollo Incident, May 9, 1967).

In this process, NASA has provided a technical interface and technical monitoring function as an addition to the normal or standard process of contract monitoring, much of which is performed for us by the Department of Defense contract administration service. In cases where contractors have encountred serious technical or management difficulties, it has been our policy to assist them to develop strengths they did not have and to utilize our knowledge of the factors which brought success to one contractor to help others take advantage of this experience. . . .

The plain fact is that our U.S. industrial system has in the past generally made its profits from large-scale production and the initial learning period on complex space development projects has not had the incentive of anticipated profits from large production orders.

The biggest job to come along, as everyone in the aerospace business knew, was going to be the Apollo project. That in itself presented a problem for industry and government. For how many firms were capable of even considering such a program? One big firm had a very simple approach: it called on NASA to give it the job, furnish the money, and allow it to move in its own way.

That was not precisely how NASA intended to approach the problem.

In August 1961, a few dozen firms were briefed on the detailed requirements of the Apollo spacecraft, and a month later a much smaller number of requests for proposals was sent out. Actually, there were only half a dozen firms in the country that had the capability of doing this kind of job, and not more than twenty that could even make a stab at it.

In October five big aeronautical firms submitted proposals for the development of the Apollo spacecraft. The appraisal of these proposals was far more detailed, precise, and complex than it had been for the Rocketdyne engine contract or the McDonnell Mercury proposal two years earlier. No fewer than 190 people were called in to examine the proposals, in terms of technical facilities, capabilities, and management ability. They went thoroughly into the subcontracting system of each bidder and estimated the cost of going ahead with any of these contractors.

In the final analysis the contest was narrowed down to two proposers: the Martin Company and North American Aviation. Because it had participated in several studies on the program, the Martin Company had an edge, and the source evaluation board at NASA selected it. But theirs was not the final decision: Webb retained that for himself and Dr. Dryden and Dr. Seamans, his principal assistants. They considered all that the board had to offer, and came to the conclusion that the board had weighted the proposal for Martin because of its participation in the study programs, and had not given sufficient credit to North American for its performance in producing the X-15, the very successful beginning of the air-into-space program. Perhaps there were one or two other factors: North American had the engineers available to do the work, whereas it was indicated that Martin had cut back its engineering staff, and the men who had participated in the old study programs and even some who had made the proposal were no longer readily available, if available at all.[5]

In addition there was the remarkable record of chairman Kindelberger of North American, for whom the NASA officials had the greatest respect.

With all the ponderables and imponderables, adminis-

[5] Various NASA officials in conversations with author.

trator Webb considered long and hard. He considered North American's overall performance in work on manned flight systems, and the fact that the company had a consistent record of low-cost, high-quality engineering. Actually the North American proposal was lower in cost than Martin's, but this was not a vital factor. Webb listed three factors: technical capability, resources, and personnel.

From all this, Webb led his assistants to the decision: they would negotiate with North American Aviation for a contract, and if the negotiations were unsuccessful, they would then turn to Martin, even though Martin's adjusted cost figures for the program were roughly 34 per cent more than North American's. But of course it was assumed that a contract would be arranged with North American, for everyone knew that the Apollo spacecraft job was a real plum, which would mean several billions of dollars worth of business to the company.

That same autumn, NASA negotiated with various contractors to build the launch vehicle that would put Apollo into space. Boeing won the contract to build the first booster stage, North American the contract to build the second stage, and Douglas Aircraft the contract for the third stage. Thus these three companies plus McDonnell, which had the Mercury-Gemini program, were assured of futures in the space business.

Not so the other companies which had a stake in the space business. Martin was still involved with missiles, but losing the Apollo contract was a stiff blow, and it showed in the next few years as Martin's big Baltimore facility closed down bit by bit, and operations moved largely to plants in Denver and Orlando, Florida, where parts of the space business were stationed. Eventually Martin would make a re-entry into the big space business by securing the contract to build the Viking spacecraft that would be used to explore Mars.

The space business—supplying NASA and the military—was bringing about some basic changes in the corporate configurations of various companies. A study of two very successful corporations yields some interesting indications of the trends:

In the 1930's North American Aviation was organized in a small plant near Dundalk, Maryland, with seventy-five employees and one contract with the government for an Army air corps trainer plane. In 1969 it was the twenty-ninth largest corporation in the United States, and was expanding into new fields every year at a rate and in a direction that could be called either comforting or alarming, depending on how one regarded the concept of the "military-industrial complex."

North American faced a crisis in August 1945, when the war against Japan ended. At that time the company had expanded tremendously to meet the military needs of the nation, and on V-J day had contracts to build some eight thousand planes. But within twenty-four hours, 90 per cent of those contracts were canceled. North American's employment fell from ninety-one thousand to fewer than five thousand men and women.

This was the second great lesson for airframe companies in the need for diversification: it was almost a carbon copy of the problem at the end of World War I. There was, however, a great exception: within a matter of months it became apparent to the United States government that the end of World War II had not brought the kind of peace that had come about at the end of World War I. The allies were not in as fine a degree of accord—indeed they were split on nearly every subject, witness the divisions of Germany, Austria, and Korea; the establishment of spheres of influence; and the Cold War.

By war's end North American was conducting various experimental programs that concerned the sonic barrier and even (in dreams) the conquest of space. And chairman Kindelberger earned his reputation for vision by diversifying via the building of guided missiles and the byways into which this led the company. There would be problems of electronics, rockets, and the harnessing of nuclear energy. There were still airplanes to be built, as the Korean war showed in 1950, and several airframe companies concentrated on that. But North American, while building its share of planes (P-82, FJ-1, B-45 bombers, Navion liaison and executive plane, F-86 sabre jet, F-100), pushed ahead in space. In 1946 North American secured a contract for a feasibility study on guided missiles. In 1948 it launched a 14-foot test vehicle called Nativ, then won an Air Force contract to study the Navaho intercontinental missile system. With the Navaho construction contract, the company was plunged deep into the space business.

In spite of ups and downs (the cancellation of Navaho in 1957), the general course of the North American company was one of expansion. North American built the XB-70, a triplesonic airplane; it built the X-15 research plane on a long-term contract with the Air Force. In the course of these efforts North American's engineers and scientists learned a great deal about jet engines, aerodynamics, thermodynamics, and metallurgy and materials engineering, including welding. (For example, in the Apollo project, one of the most serious fabrication problems was the control of the welding so there could be absolutely no weak spot, and to accomplish this North American created a fantastic welding machine.)

By the time North American secured the Apollo contract and one-third of the Apollo launch vehicle work, the company had become something of an octopus, which could boast that *"most of the American satellites and space probes* have been launched into orbit by engines developed at North American's Rocketdyne Division."[6] The first Rocketdyne engine of importance, for example, was used in the Redstone missile. Other Rocketdyne engines were used for Atlas, Thor, and Jupiter missiles. At one time Reaction Motors Inc., the creature of the men of the American Rocket Society, had given some indications of becoming the leading engine manufacturer. But Reaction Motors, and later Thiokol, simply could not compete in the expense of what might be called mass or assembly-line technology. By the mid-1960's Rocketdyne was producing the H-1 engine, eight of which provided 1,500,000 pounds of thrust for the first stage of Saturn C-1. Later Rocketdyne's F-1 engine would alone produce that much thrust, and five of them together would give the Saturn V vehicle 7,500,000 pounds of thrust.

Nor was Rocketdyne dominant in the big-engine field alone. The company produced the 225,000-pound J-2 for the upper stages of Saturn, and the small rocket engines used for attitude control in the Gemini spacecraft. Rocketdyne was involved in the Air Force Titan III missile, working on the attitude control system. It was certainly the leader in liquid-fuel rocket engines, and was advancing rapidly in

[6] From conversations with W. E. Van Dyke of North American Aviation, and from company reports and company histories.

solid-fuel engines, such as the navy Sparrow, air-to-air missile, and the army Redhead/Roadrunner. Equally important was this big company's developmental work, in high energy power plants and even nuclear engines. Rocketdyne had become a behemoth in its field, with its headquarters at Canoga Park, California, and its propulsion laboratory in the Santa Susana Mountains, which, it boasted, was the most extensive high-thrust test center in the free world. In other words, nowhere outside the Soviet Union was there a facility that could match Rocketdyne's for producing and testing big rocket engines. Besides all this, the Rocketdyne division operated an Air Force plant at Neosho, Missouri, making and testing liquid-propellant rocket engines. It also operated a solid-propellant plant at McGregor, Texas, and maintained an advanced propulsion research facility near Reno. One can see what the NASA people meant by North American "capabilities," which the company's officials frankly and correctly said no one could touch.

Quite aside from the big pieces of hardware, North American showed a staggering grasp on the space business by 1966. The Autonetics division in Anaheim, California, was designing, developing, and producing inertial and navigation instruments, computers and data processing equipment, radar, flight control and armament control systems, microelectronic circuits. It built the autonavigation systems for the atomic submarines that went under the Polar ice cap. It was deeply involved in guidance and control systems for the Minuteman ICBM, the Hound Dog missile. It was building ships' inertial navigation systems for the nuclear submarines and nuclear carriers. It was building inertial bombing-navigation systems for the Navy and engaged in many other military construction and research programs. It was also doing research relative to lunar and interplanetary missions, oceanographic exploration and oceanology, solid state devices, plasma physics, film magnetic memories, learning machines, and microelectronics, computers for weapons systems and for industry. Autonetics had expanded to include a new plant in the Bluefield-Princeton area of West Virginia.

The Space and Information Systems division of the company, which had secured the Apollo contract, was building the command module and service module for the lunar mission, making the second stage of the Saturn V launch vehicle, and building Paraglider, an inflatable kite-type of wing which could be used to deliver cargo and space vehicles. S&ID, as it was called in the company, was also making the ill-fated Hound Dog Missile, for use with the B-52.

One key to North American's philosophy is found in the company history of 1966:

> *Studies in astronautics are not only providing working data for the company's current space programs, but are also adding to our basic knowledge of astronomy, lunary and planetary geology and space power. These studies are yielding vital information on the techniques for satellite rendezvous; the nature of the atmosphere, gravitational field and other physical characteristics of the moon and planets.*

In testimony before Congress, James Webb said that one of the precepts of the NASA way of handling the space business was to pass along the experience of one company to another which might be working in the same field. And yet this could hardly be the case, if the companies were to retain their traditional competitive attitudes and situations. It was all right to pass on certain technological data—for example, the lessons learned in McDonnell's Mercury and Gemini programs would certainly be passed on to North American for inclusion in the Apollo adventure. But the information was not always very useful. Usually American industry has earned its profits by first inventing or improving some device and then putting it into assembly line manufacture; the costs of the research and development have been quickly made up in the cost savings of assembly lines. This was true of automobiles and even fighter planes, but it has not been true of space vehicles, and it seemed doubtful in 1969 that it would be true of them for a long time to come. The generation of information was valuable to other industries, but the space business was moving so fast that every development was a new adventure.

North American in the mid-1960's was not solely concerned with space. An Atomics International division of the company was prime contractor to the Atomic Energy Commission for Systems for Nuclear Auxiliary Power, which was usually known by the acronym SNAP. The idea was to generate electric power for use in space vehicles, at lunar bases, on the ground, and undersea. An offshoot of this business was the manufacture of nuclear reactors for medical, industrial, and other research. Atomics International was also engaged in building reactors for the AEC, and developing a sodium-cooled fast breeder reactor and a heavy-water-moderated organic cooled reactor. For Spain it designed a reactor, and for the New York State Utilities it made a study of a high-temperature reactor. In 1956 North American had built the first reactor for private industrial use and was the leader in its field.

At Los Angeles and Columbus, Ohio, North American continued to produce aircraft in number. One was the T-39, a jet utility trainer for the Air Force and Navy, with a civilian version sold as an executive aircraft. The work on the X-15 gave North American valuable experience in supersonic transport and aerospace transport. As for facilities, the company's could hardly be matched by many others. North American's Aerospace laboratory contained a "hard vacuum" chamber that simulated the vacuum of space. The company's engineers built their own hybrid computer system to perform navigation and simulated space flight, which gave them an almost exclusive capability to simulate conditions of unexplored areas of manned flight.

Columbus was far more an airplane facility, building there the Vigilante attack and reconnaissance plane for the carrier navy, plus the T-2 Buckeye trainer and the YAT-28E turboprop plane for special air warfare, and the OV-10A counterinsurgency aircraft for close ground support and attack missions. For the Army Columbus built the Redhead/Roadrunner missile, and for the Air Force it went into radome building and antennas. Columbus in 1966 was conducting research in lunar landings (although Grumman got the lunar module contract), vertical takeoff and lift, and even antisubmarine warfare.

In Conejo Valley, California, the company maintained its Science Center, for by the middle of the 1960's North American could afford a research and development program that engaged scientists and technicians in "pure research": fundamental work in physics, chemistry, metallurgy, and mathematics. "These research programs," said the company history, "supplement activities in labs of other North American divisions, which are all directed toward advancing product technologies to meet specific developmental goals."

That was 1966. By 1968 there had been more changes.

The company had become North American Rockwell, merging with the giant Rockwell-Standard Manufacturing Company, and was even bigger and more important. Its total sales to government and business were more than $2.5 billion, its net earnings nearly $74 million. In 1968 North American Rockwell acquired Textile Machine Works of Reading, Pennsylvania, a producer of machinery for knitting ladies' hosiery and other goods. It acquired Remmert-Werner Inc., an aircraft distributor; the Hatteras Yacht Company of North Carolina, which builds luxury cabin cruisers; the Acme Chain Corporation of Holyoke, Mass.; and Luber-Finer of Los Angeles, a firm that makes filters for trucks and large diesel engines.

The changes were coming with revolutionary speed. Also in 1968 North American formed a subsidiary with Scientific Advances Inc., called Electrospin Corporation, to develop a new process for electrostatic spinning of yarn. It formed a subsidiary with Gould-National Batteries Inc. to produce timers and batteries using solid electrolytes. It was involved in deals with Mobil Oil, to recover oil and gas from deep offshore locations, and a Swiss company, to market its power equipment in the United States under a joint venture. It had become the nation's largest manufacturer, aside from the Big Three, of components for motor vehicles: axles, brakes, springs, universal joints, etc. The automotive division included thirty-three manufacturing operations in the United States and Canada.

In the following year, 1969, one of the most important developments in the company's business was discussed by board chairman Willard F. Rockwell, Jr. It is called technology transfer.

"Technology transfer—in brief—" said Mr. Rockwell,

"is the flow of advanced knowledge, skills, processes, and devices between the company's groups and divisions for profitable use in broader markets."[7]

This transfer had become a primary company aim, for it was recognized that "technological progress is the hallmark of our time and the key to competitive advantage." Such transfer was a prime reason for the North American-Rockwell merger, since North American was a leader in aerospace work and electronics, while Rockwell-Standard was an important commercial and industrial manufacturer.

Bringing them together had created something new—a basic aerospace company that could withstand the volatility of aerospace marketing changes. By the end of the first quarter of 1969, North American Rockwell could say that while its aerospace business was down, its automotive, yacht, civil airplane, and other commercial businesses were up about 15 per cent and its profits were up 40 per cent. To fill up the holes in the space business, the company was competing for the big F-15 Air Force fighter contract and for the Air Force manned strategic aircraft.

To an extent less spectacular than North American, other big aerospace companies were combining forces and expanding operations. McDonnell merged with Douglas. Boeing extended its activities building bigger airplanes. The course seemed to be, in the 1960's, expand or die. This gave room for some serious thought.

So did the progress of another company whose basic start was in the space business—Thompson-Ramo-Wooldridge, or TRW. In 1960, when the competitors of TRW forced the company to divest itself of its advisory work for

[7] North American Rockwell Quarterly Report, Spring 1969, pp. 14–15.

the Air Force, Space Technology Laboratories division of the company turned over $20 million in business to the nonprofit company Aerospace. This part of TRW—which was to be known later as the TRW Systems Group—had an annual business of $60 million still, but $40 million of that was in ICBM contracts which would eventually come to an end. So TRW saw the handwriting on the wall, and began to diversify in many ways.[8] First the systems group went after other government business. It got a contract from the Army to work on Advent, an Army communications satellite. It won a contract with NASA to take on the Orbiting Geophysical Observatory, an $18,400,000 contract, and a highly classified Air Force project for spacecraft. These contracts were taken on an incentive basis. Within three years this one division had jumped from $60 million in business to $100 million.

TRW, by its own statement, has come to be a new kind of corporation, "a diversified technology company, whose scientific and manufacturing talents contribute importantly to the growth of several major industries."[9]

In 1957 military contracts had accounted for 70 per cent of TRW's business, but by 1967 only 30 per cent of sales were purely military, and no single contract amounted to more than 10 per cent of the company's business. The Thompson part of the business, which had provided the working capital in the early days, was based on an original engine valve manufacturing operation that expanded to the extent that in 1967 most Americans cars used nearly 200 TRW parts. But the technology provided by the Ramo-

[8] *Fortune*, February 1963.
[9] "This is TRW"—a company brochure.

Wooldridge firm was what put it on the corporate map. By 1967 TRW could claim to be to the unmanned part of the space business what North American was to the bigger business—"the industry leader in the design and manufacture of unmanned spacecraft."[10] TRW built satellites for Comsat, the commercial satellite enterprise. It continued to work on systems engineering for the Air Force, and on testing and systems integration for the Navy's antisubmarine program.

TRW was also moving into new fields, such as "civil systems," which meant urban transportation, hospital design, and even environmental pollution control. It was active in the television business, producing parts (three-quarters of the TV manufacturers of color sets use TRW color convergence yokes, for example. TRW could boast in 1967 that it was spending $150 million a year on research and development, but the key was that, as TRW said, "a large part of it is being supported by our customers." The point there, of course, is that government contracts support a good deal of such research, and the government contracts tend to go to those who have done the studies in the field: *e.g.*, the NASA source evaluation board's inclination to give Martin Company the Apollo contract because Martin had been doing the studies while North American had not. So again it was a case of "them as has, gets," and this could be another problem for the consideration of Congress and the public.

TRW by 1967 was a company of sixty thousand employees, doing business at two hundred locations. It could be said, then, that a job given TRW would help the econ-

10 *Ibid.*, p. 2.

omy in two hundred different places, and that certainly would destroy one of the old arguments for passing the business around—the Congressional pork barrel approach. The fact remained that as of 1967 TRW could claim to be "a prime contractor or major supplier of hardware and services for nearly 90 per cent of *all the manned and unmanned space projects of the United States.*"[11]

In the course of its remarkable expansion, North American Rockwell has acquired forty subsidiaries, affiliates, and licensees in twenty countries on all six continents. It owns 42 per cent of Braseixos Rockwell, S.A., South America's largest manufacturer of automotive components, and has infiltrated the markets of Chile, Mexico, Japan, Great Britain, Israel, Australia, and South Africa. TRW in recent years has acquired whole or majority interest in many foreign firms. In the automotive line alone TRW has twelve thousand employees in fourteen subsidiaries on five continents. It owns outright such firms as Clifford Motor Components of England, Teves-Thompson of Germany, Gemmer-France of France, and it has a plant in Uitenhage, South Africa. In the space field, the company is in business with SAAB in Sweden; Hawker-Siddeley Dynamics in England; ERNO of Germany; and Engins-Matra of France, with which it has formed a joint space venture, called MATREL. This company in 1967 won a competition for a European Space Research Organization program. TRW is also in business with Mitsubishi in Japan to build world-wide ground stations for commercial communications satellites.

And to think that just a few years ago the American government was concerned about the existence of European-

11 *Ibid.*, p. 11.

based cartels, big combines of industries which seemed to threaten the welfare of independent companies. In the old terms, the United States government and U.S. industry had become the biggest cartelist force in history.

The Dealer That Failed

In 1931 Alexander P. De Seversky rented a hangar from the Edo Aircraft Company at College Point, Long Island, and set out to produce a revolutionary three seat, twin float amphibian airplane. This can be considered the beginning of Republic Aircraft Corporation.

De Seversky produced an excellent plane, the SEV-3XAR, which in 1933 achieved a speed record of 235 mph. In various forms, it was fairly widely sold; the Colombian government bought six of the planes and the American government bought thirty.

The success of this experiment put the De Seversky Aircraft Corporation on its feet, more or less. The firm later produced a plane that was bought and termed by the Army air corps the P-35, and several other types that were sold throughout the world. But Seversky, unfortunately, was an inventor and aeronautical genius, not a businessman, and his company fell on evil days even when it was producing and selling aircraft successfully. In 1939 it was reorganized as Republic Aircraft, and Seversky was forced out of it.[1]

Republic Aircraft prospered mildly until the war years, producing the P-35 for Japan and other countries under contracts. In 1939 the Swedish government ordered a hundred of an improved version of the plane, known as the EP-106, and then fifty 2PA 204A dive bombers. The order was being filled (sixty fighters had been delivered) when the European war caused the United States government to embargo shipment of war planes, and the remainder of the planes were delivered to the U.S. Army air corps as P-35As. The bombers, except for a handful, were delivered to the Air Corps as AT-12s.

During World War II Republic Aircraft prospered immensely in its production of the P-47 fighter. Alexander Kartveli, Seversky's designer of the P-35, had remained with the company in its reorganization. Even in 1944, when the P-47 was going great guns, Kartveli was off on an entirely different tack, working on the design for a new jet plane, the F-84 Thunderjet. Republic was well-to-do and convinced of the need for research and development in the field, so without grudging, 500,000 engineering man hours were spent to produce the F-84. It was the first Air Force

[1] *RAF Flying Review*, June 1961.

fighter to go into the 600-mile-an-hour class, when it was tested in February 1946, at Muroc, California.[2]

Then came the tooling up process, as the Air Force indicated that it wanted a big order of these planes, Republic's plant at Farmingdale, Long Island, was increased to cover 1,650,000 square feet of factory area devoted to military planes. General Electric would supply the axial-flow turbojet engine, and dozens of other suppliers would bring in lesser parts. Republic began doing what it knew so well how to do: train employees in the exacting requirements of production for this plane. By the middle of 1947 the Thunderjet was in production.

The Air Force put a good deal of pressure on Republic to speed up its processes. The Air Force wanted those planes and wanted them fast. There came modification after modification, until Republic was producing the F-84E, then the F and then the G. When the Korean war broke out in June 1950, Republic had about five hundred employees. The company was producing about 10 F-84s a month. At the end of 1950 Republic had seven thousand employees; at the end of 1951 it employed eighteen thousand men and women and worked with 2,200 subcontractors and suppliers. The profit picture was very pleasing: after taxes in 1951 Republic earned $2,934,613.[3]

So good was business that the following year Republic opened a New York City office and staffed it with 350 engineers. Nearly five hundred engineers were recruited by the firm that year, along with 5,800 new production workers. The company was expanding in almost every direction. Republic added 216,000 square feet of production facility

[2] "The Story of Republic's Thunderjet," *U.S. Air Services,* April 1952.
[3] *Aviation Week,* April 1952.

at Port Washington, Long Island. It took a building in rural Greenlawn with another forty thousand square feet. It added 180,000 square feet by purchase at Montauk, at the southeastern end of Long Island, and added forty thousand square feet to its Farmingdale plant. It could well afford to make these production additions. In 1952 the backlog of orders amounted to $580 million, and if the various customers who had signified intent to purchase all came through with their orders, the company would have another quarter-million dollars in business.

Mundy I. Peale, president of Republic Aircraft Corporation, was a very contented man:

"When the American people turn to the aircraft industry in periods of emergency, they call upon it not for a prototype of a superior plane but for hundreds of perfectly functioning aircraft rolling off the production lines," he said. "This means that the industry has an obligation to have in operation vast and complicated production facilities. . . ."

There was Peale's philosophy, in a sense very close to that suggested by NASA administrator Webb when he defined the *modus vivendi* of American industry in general.

The trouble with Peale's philosophy was that it put Republic in the situation of a horse wearing blinders. The company could see straight ahead, down a long beautiful slope, with profits all the way. It was not looking to right or left, where North American Aviation and General Electric were devoting millions of dollars to space research; where Simon Ramo and Dean Wooldridge were preparing to quit their jobs with Hughes Aircraft and swing out on their own in the space field. No, Republic was looking at the aircraft industry, and envisaging a beautiful future for itself.

A year later (1953) Republic's sales dropped from

$412,235,000 to $411,810,000, but was there any cause to worry about that little dip? The net profit was up from $8,096,000 to $8,314,000—proof that the money to be made by industry was in assembly line production where unit costs would keep going down as the product was manufactured in quantity. By this time Republic Aircraft had built and delivered twenty-two thousand airplanes.

There was research. But the emphasis was on research in titanium studies, for titanium could be used to produce more and better airplanes. A very little bit of space research was under way in 1952. As the company said later, its space research dated back to the 1940's, but that was really begging the issue. In the mid-1950's Republic was still putting its bets on the aircraft industry. In 1954 President Peale predicted a steady, reasonable pace for the aircraft industry, based on a production rate of about twelve thousand planes per year.

But the industrial world around Republic was changing very rapidly. Nineteen fifty-five was the year that North American split into six divisions, four of them concerned with the new technologies of space and only two concerned primarily with aircraft production. It was also the year that Ramo-Wooldridge took on more responsibility with the United States Air Force, based on the entirely new concept of a company that ran systems for the defense program.

In 1956 Republic showed signs of sensing the changes that were coming so quickly in America.[4] It established a guided missile division, naming as general manager Robert G. Melrose. (North American had begun its first guided missile study in 1946, and by this time was *producing* the Navaho.) Despite Republics' claim that it had been in the

4 *U.S. Air Services*, August 1956.

guided missile field since 1944, it had not much to show for the activity. Now it would concentrate on air-to-air missiles and air-to-surface firing control systems. In other words, Republic still considered its missile program an auxiliary to the military aircraft program.

The company's awakening continued. President Peale announced that it would begin a basic research program under Dr. Theodore Theodorsen, with Alexander Kartveli very much in the picture. The program would span the "range between purely theoretical research and applied engineering," said President Peale. What he meant was that Republic was going to go into research and development in a big way for the first time. His scientists and engineers would study the thermal barrier, atomic energy, hypersonic flight, mathematics, physics, supersonics, and nuclear physics, while the 120 new engineers and thirty mechanics worked on the problems of missiles.[5] (This was 1956—the year that North American got down to cases in the building of the X-15 research plane and the XB-70 triple sonic airplane.)

The kind and extent of this research is indicated by one program of 1957. Republic spent $200 for a study of a pinch plasma engine for satellite control.[6] To be sure, the next year Republic spent $47,000 on the same problem. (North American was producing atomic reactors for private industry. Ramo-Wooldridge, having merged with Thompson, set up Space Technology Laboratories as a separate division of the company.)

By 1958 the company was aware of its steadily worsening position in the industry. The problem was many-fold. President Peale could see that by the 1960's, barring a ma-

[5] *Aviation Week*, May 21, 1956.
[6] *Aviation Week and Space Technology*, January 21, 1963.

jor war somewhere, there would not be enough demand for military aircraft to keep all the airframe companies of 1958 in business. One of Republic's first moves was to establish a helicopter division. Since the company had no helicopters, it proposed to market the French five-seat Alouette and secured the exclusive rights to sell in South America. The company also announced in August that it would enter the field of astronautics.[7]

Republic spoke up bravely now in terms of big money, for Peale had seen how the ante was going up each year for those companies that wanted to stay in what was by this time the aerospace business. Peale announced that Republic would spend $35 million for research and development to put itself into the space and missile business. It would build a fourteen-million-dollar center at Farmingdale. It would add many competent engineers and scientists to the staff. It would establish laboratories for space environment, re-entry simulation and aerodynamics, materials development, electronics, guidance and control systems, and advanced fluid systems. The company would study space platforms, interplanetary vehicles, lunar exploration programs.

But even now President Peale could not resist promoting the airplane. Part of the money, he said, would be spent to "intensify studies designed to extend the capabilities of the F-105 fighter bomber." Republic had been picked to build that plane for the Air Force. It was elementary economics that if Republic could extend the bomber's capabilities, the Air Force would continue to need new, revised aircraft to keep up to date, and the contract could run on and on. "Our long-range objective," Peale said, "is to cap-

[7] *Aviation Week*, August 4, 1958.

ture a position of leadership for the company in the field of astronautics."[8]

If so, Republic had waited a long time to get started. But having started, the company began with Peale's enthusiastic backing to try to push itself forward. One of its first moves was to go to Washington and brief the NACA people on man-in-space studies, with an eye to securing the first contract.

The trouble was still that Peale and his executives were primarily airplane oriented. Early in 1959, Peale made his position clear. American air defense philosophy was moving toward a mixed system of aircraft and missiles, he said, and there would always be a place for the manned vehicle. He then devoted most of his discussion (before the New York Society of Security Analysts) to the F-105, the airplane that was bringing in Republic's profits. The company had a backlog of $42 million in orders, he said. (Far cry from the half-billion dollars in orders of seven years earlier.)

"When we reach that inevitable point of no return, we have plans for second and third generation F-105s, radical new models like twin-engine-short-takeoff-and-landing and vertical-takeoff-and-landing versions, a strike recon version, a multipurpose export version for the NATO countries."[9]

Peale was still an aviation-minded man.

He did speak of the six million dollars in sales expected from the missiles and space division in 1958. He talked about the research laboratories, on which eight to ten million dollars would be spent that year. But the problem was that the money was being spent to *build* the laboratories at this time; they were not completed for another year.

[8] *Ibid.*
[9] *Aviation Week,* February 16, 1959.

Even in 1959 Peale was aware of a general criticism from the industry: "Unfortunately there seems to be an impression that this was a sudden do-or-die decision on our part," whereas in fact, he said, it was a part of the company's policy of keeping on top of changing technology. The difficulty, apparently, was that Republic did not realize how fast the technology was changing, that it was running furiously simply to stand in the same place.

In 1960 when a British magazine writer visited Republic's main plant at Farmingdale, he gained the distinct impression that the company's enthusiasms concerned, in this order, the 105 Thunderchief airplane, ideas for future aircraft, and research and development in several fields.[10]

So it went for three years. The F-105 contract remained; it was like a lifeline trailing down into the depths of the ocean, a line in which the pressure was slowly diminishing. For three years President Peale searched for a way out, each year the process becoming more frantic. Between 1960 and 1963 Republic investigated the possibilities of merger with more than four hundred companies, ranging from the aerospace business to building construction. Nothing came of any of them.

In 1963 the company knew that the F-105 would fall out on them in 1964. On paper everything looked fine. The company had a backlog of $560 million in business, but of that $46 million was in the F-105, and much of the rest was for subcontracts for parts of the F-4, which McDonnell was producing. The rub was that Republic had taken the F-4 contracts in desperation, under conditions where it was losing money on everything it produced for McDonnell.

One statistic indicated what was happening. The com-

[10] *Flight,* October 21, 1960.

pany had generated some two million dollars in contracts in the field of satellite control—but it had spent three million dollars on facilities, equipment, and personnel to develop the knowledge to get the contracts. And there was no real hope of assembly line manufacture in this branch of the space business.

Republic was trying manfully. It had teamed up with Minneapolis Honeywell and Texas Instrument to secure a $100,000 study contract for an Orbiting Solar Observatory. But two other study contracts had been let to Ball Brothers and Space Technology Laboratories. To get a third of the $100,000 contract, Republic had spent $500,000 on study alone, developing its proficiencies very expensively because it had waited so long as the technology rolled on ahead. And now it could justify this kind of expenditure only by looking forward to the $50–$100 million potential in business in years to come—if Republic really could catch up and get some of that business.

The prospects were not promising.

Republic had spent two and a half years and $750,000 in its bid for the Apollo space capsule, and had not even come close. It was not just a question of money—as has been noted elsewhere comparative costs were less the guiding factor in NASA decisions than engineering and facility capability to do these big jobs. It was here that Republic did not prove itself.

From that Apollo failure Republic salvaged a small contract to build two re-entry vehicles for study of Apollo's re-entry environment, but that was all. It seemed that study contract followed study contract, with never a production contract on which the company could make a profit. In 1963 Republic secured another study contract: to design and plan development of a synchronous altitude meteorological satellite. It was to be a four-month study with a cost to NASA of $136,640.[11]

But all this was too little, and too late. In 1963 the missile space business, with seven hundred thousand employees, was competing with the automotive industry as the top employer in the United States.[12] Federal research and development spending had jumped to $15 billion by 1963 and 66 per cent of this money was spent by industry. It was true, as Stanford Research Institute estimated, that the various companies were devoting about 18 per cent of their engineering and scientific man hours to research and development proposals, and that 75 per cent of these amounted to no contract, but this was a hazard of the trade. The big companies that had secured government contracts early in the game had a revolving door working for them; research moneys built into one project could always be diverted to another, and in essence the government was paying the freight. But Republic had never achieved the success in the space business that would give it that protective pad.

The plight of Republic had become public knowledge, and a very bright man in the aeronautical business decided to take advantage of it. He was Sherman Fairchild, head of Fairchild Hiller Corporation, who had built a big business out of an aerial photography camera. Very quietly in 1964, Fairchild and his associates began acquiring Republic Aircraft Corporation stock on the market, using so many different names and such good cover that no one suspected them. Before the end of the year Fairchild had secured enough stock on the falling market to gain control of the

[11] *Missiles and Rockets*, February 25, 1963.
[12] *Missiles and Rockets*, October 28, 1963.

company, and he simply stepped in and took over. Why would he want it? Fairchild indicated he thought new management could put Republic on its feet. Others, more cynical, suggested that he had bought the company as a real estate speculation, because the Farmingdale property, located in the middle of Long Island, had long since been surrounded by housing and business and was extremely valuable land in the commuting zone of New York City.

Fairchild put his finger on the basic problem of Republic in the 1960's. "Republic's main trouble," he said, "was that they had so much overhead that everything they bid on they lost and they were losing money to the point where they were going down the drain pretty fast."[13]

If that was an oversimplification, still Republic was in trouble. One of its last gasps had been an expensive and very strong study program in an attempt to secure the lunar module contract for the Apollo program. Engineers had spent many months working on this plan, and when it failed, and the contract went to Grumman (which had almost secured the Apollo command capsule contract and had impressed everyone at NASA in this endeavor), Republic's bolt was nearly shot.

In 1964 the end came. Republic became a division of the Fairchild Hiller Corporation. Of all the top management only vice president John Stack, of engineering, remained with the company. President Peale left for the west, and ten vice presidents stepped down and out. The eight thousand employees were cut back to 3,750. The 2.5 million square feet of floor space was cut to 1.5 million. The company had lost 3.3 million dollars in 1964, and thereafter trimmed its losses by cutting to meet the income. Repub-

[13] *Flying*, October 1966.

lic under the new management set out to capture space contracts and make an impact on the space business. But it was no longer Republic and would never be the same: a half-billion-dollar company had gone down the drain. To some extent the talents, laboratories, and investment of time were all lost. Thousands of men and women who had counted on weekly paychecks from this company had to find other jobs in the area, or move in order to follow their line of work. (Some were taken up by Grumman, which is also on Long Island.) But aeronautical workers were long used to moving about. And the trend was unmistakably toward merger: in 1970 the two immense competitors, North American Rockwell and McDonnell Douglas, would combine efforts to seek new space contracts—and so would Boeing and Lockheed. All the talk about competition in the industry was boiling down to more and more talk and less and less competition.

12

The Telephone Company Satellite and
The Virtues of Competition

In the summer of 1960, as the Bell Telephone system was preparing with the help of NASA to launch the one-hundred-foot balloon named Echo, the company's attorneys were proposing to the Federal Communications Commission plans for a private world-wide communications system using repeater satellites. Early in 1961 the commission authorized American Telephone and Telegraph to establish an experimental satellite link across the Atlantic. In that manner project Telstar was born.

AT&T representatives met with officials of NASA and arrived at an agreement: the company would design and construct a pair of 170-pound satellites at the company's expense, and would reimburse NASA for the costs of launching the satellite and the use of the government tracking stations, the Minitrack system.[1] The American Telephone and Telegraph Company is a private enterprise, of course, and monopolistic in nature; thus even though much good was to come from a satellite program of this kind, government decided that private industry should pay its own way. This project was unique in that it was the first attempt by private industry to make a business use of space. But the Bell system was looking a long way ahead in order to provide the communications facilities that could be required by an expanding twentieth-century economy. In the middle of the 1960's the Bell system was using nine hundred telephone circuits for overseas communications. The company estimated that by 1970 it would need eighteen hundred circuits; by 1980, ten thousand for telephones, plus another two thousand for other types of communications. Much of this would be avoided if a series of satellites could be proved workable.

Telstar was feasible in 1960 because over the years the Bell company had acquired a number of patents that lent themselves to exploitation. There were sixteen in all, dating back to the patent for Joseph C. Chaffee's low-static radio receiver, granted in 1937. Other basic inventions were a large horn-shaped antenna patented by Alfred C. Beck and Harald T. Friis in 1947, and a solid state microwave amplifier called MASER, patented in 1961.

---

[1] *Satellite Communications Physics*, published by the Bell Telephone Laboratories, pp. 8–16.

The key to all, however, was the transistor, the tiny electronic device that does the work of a large vacuum tube. It would have been impossible to put up a satisfactory satellite using vacuum tubes, but with the invention of the transistor in the 1940's by Bell personnel, the satellite became a definite possibility. Other inventions were constant-voltage diodes, used in telemetering, and solar batteries, invented by Bell scientists in the 1950's, which drew their power from the sun and thus made it possible for a satellite to repower itself day after day.[2] None of these inventions were specifically earmarked for space research; they were the natural outcome of the multimillion-dollar Bell Laboratories research program, a development which shows why this semimonopolistic private enterprise in America functions more efficiently than any government-owned telephone system in the world. (I say semimonopolistic, because although the Bell system is monopolistic where it does operate, it has competitors in General Telephone and a number of private systems and even in manufacturing of telephone equipment.)

The Bell system estimated that during the period after 1945 it spent $1.5 billion on communications research and development, about a billion dollars of this in fields that would be pertinent to satellite communication. The studies completed, work began in several fields: deciding on the launch vehicle, preparing the satellites themselves, building a monitoring system that would make the satellites useful.

NASA and Bell engineers decided the Delta rocket (an offshoot of the Thor) was the most satisfactory for the company's purposes. The satellite would be placed in an orbit with an apogee of three thousand miles and a perigee of

[2] *The New York Times*, September 5, 1962.

about five hundred miles, inclined about forty-five degrees to the equator. This was not the optimum orbit for a communications satellite (the apogee might better be eight thousand miles), but the limitations of the Delta vehicle set the orbit.

There were other known limitations. Ideally, the satellite should present one face to the earth all the time, but practically, the satellite had to spin, which meant that the antennae could not be directed usefully at all times. Also there was the known problem of radiation, which would reduce the life of the solar battery cells—but nobody knew by quite how much. It was definitely an experiment.[3]

Much of the work on Telstar was done in the impressive and handsome laboratories at Holmdel, New Jersey. A ground station was established at Andover, Maine, and in March 1961 two laboratory engineers drove the first stake through two feet of snow on a timbered site near that town. Here would be constructed the big horn-reflector antenna, a conical horn 90 feet long, 94 feet high, and weighing 380 tons. Excavation was begun in May, and the antenna was completed at the end of September. In April 1961, all the equipment was in place.

Meanwhile at Holmdel the scientists and engineers were putting together the satellite itself. It would be spherical in shape because thus the most effective use of the antenna could be made, and many of the outer solar cells would face the sun no matter what the orientation of the satellite.

A two-year life was planned for the Telstar satellites, and new solar cells developed by the Signal Corps were used to bring as much power as possible with as little radiation damage as possible.

[3] *Bell Laboratories Record,* April 1963.

Nearly all the electronic assemblies of the satellite were contained in a single "electronics package" which was 20 inches in diameter and 12 inches in height. Included were a power plant with a storage battery, fed by the outer solar cells, a micro-wave repeater, a telemetry system, and a command system that would take and execute orders.

Altogether, some two thousand suppliers and subcontractors worked on parts of Telstar or provided materials. Remarkably 80 per cent of these companies were small business firms employing fewer than five hundred people. Here, then, was a demonstration that small business had a role in the space business. NASA had been saying for a long time that small business would find its most profitable applications in supplying the prime contractors of NASA programs. There *was* room for nearly everybody who had something applicable to the space business, and it was simply a matter of finding out how best to sell and to whom.

As the months rolled along, American Telephone and Telegraph spent a great deal of money on this experiment. To build the Andover installation, it spent four million dollars on forty different Maine contractors, plus another eleven million dollars on the equipment and transportation. People were brought in to man the station at a cost in payroll, services, and taxes of two million dollars.

Bell Laboratories built six Telstar satellites, at a cost of about $1.3 million each. In December 1961, Bell sent a full scale mockup of a satellite to the Douglas Aircraft Company in Santa Monica, which was building the Delta—the third-stage rocket to which the satellite would be fitted.

The facilities at Cape Canaveral were made ready in the spring. Bell Laboratories would prepare the command guidance system, which they had contracted to do for all the Delta rockets. Launch Complex 17 was set aside for Telstar, with two launch pads, fueling, power, and support facilities, such as the big gantry which erected the rocket and made it possible to service it. The satellite and the rocket would be mated in a blast-proof spin building, and then the whole taken to the site.

Two miles away from the launch site was located the Laboratories Command Guidance Center, which held the computers' antennae and tracking and guiding devices. Bell Laboratories sent down three special trailers, to hold the satellites early on, and also equipped to monitor the satellite's performance later on. The first van was equipped with controlled atmosphere to reduce the danger of contamination or damage from changes in humidity and temperature; the second contained the telemetry equipment; and the third was the Command Tracker van.

The satellites were transferred from the shipping vehicle to the first of the three satellite vans. (Two satellites were brought down, one for back-up in case of mechanical failures.) When the satellite was checked out, it was taken to the spin test building and there lowered onto the third stage of the rocket, which contained a five-hundred-pound charge of live propellant. The weight of the satellite rested against a spring which would later separate the satellite from the vehicle. The vehicle was then balanced, as a garageman balances auto wheels, by placement of weights.

Meanwhile Douglas engineers had been preparing the booster and second stage of the rocket for several weeks in the Douglas hangar. The first two stages were moved to the launch pad, and a week before the launch the flight satellite and third stage were hoisted on top, in a special housing that was air-conditioned for protection. The countdown began, eighteen hours in advance of firing, with NASA's mission control running the show from the blockhouse at Complex 17. The service tower was rolled back, the countdown continued, and at 3:35 A.M. on July 10, 1962, the Delta rocket began to move into the sky. It achieved an orbit of 514 miles (perigee), 3,040 miles (apogee), and a 44.8-degree inclination to the equator—as successful as anyone had hoped. And for all this, American Telephone and Telegraph paid NASA six million dollars.[4]

Telstar was in orbit. On the sixth orbit around the earth, at 7:26 A.M., the first transmissions to and from the satellite occurred. Telephone calls, television signals, and photographs were transmitted between Andover and Holmdel. Next day a taped television program was transmitted from France to the United States via Telstar, and a live program came from England. For four months then, Telstar worked, handling four hundred transmissions, including fifty television demonstrations. But the radiation problem was all that the engineers and scientists had feared, and in the middle of November the command circuits began to falter; on November 23 they cut out. Bell's laboratory technicians were able to correct the difficulty for a time, and on January 3, 1963, Telstar again began transmitting and behaving as it should. But on February 21 the satellite misinterpreted a command, disconnected its storage battery, and went silent.

On May 7 the second Telstar satellite was launched, and with an improved Delta rocket it was placed in an orbit with a higher apogee (6,700 miles above the earth) which meant less radiation damage. Its testing and usage began.[5]

4 The launch story is from *Bell Laboratories Record*, April 1963, a special issue devoted entirely to Telstar. Other material is from the 1964 hearings of the House Committee on Science and Astronautics, 1964, pp. 727–29.
5 *Satellite Communications Physics*, published by Bell Laboratories.

By this time there was considerable world interest in communications satellites. RCA had a contract from NASA to build Relay, a satellite to test transoceanic communications. Hughes Aircraft had a contract to build Syncom, a satellite to go into orbit 22,300 miles above the earth, the orbit to be synchronous with the rotation of the earth.

In December 1961, the political and economic interest of the world was indicated with the adoption by the United Nations of a resolution calling for the peaceful uses of outer space and for world cooperation in the development of a system of communications satellites. It was apparent that any attempt by the Bell system to dominate the communications satellite field was going to run into considerable opposition. True, outside the United States, few organizations but government were able to spend the seventy million dollars that Bell had invested in communications satellites with the Telstar equipment. Obviously Bell had not made the investment—nor would any company—without hope that it might thus save for itself the ground floor in the business applications of the new technology.

In America and abroad, the Bell system's competitors began to move. In America, on February 7, 1962, President Kennedy decided that private competition in space was not in the national interest and called on Congress to pass legislation establishing a corporation which would operate satellite communications. So, ironically, even before Telstar proved itself, the Bell system was done out of the "reward" it had hoped to win for its foresight and huge investment in technology. Space was too big for business, in that context, anyhow. In the summer of 1962, just after Telstar I went into successful orbit and showed that signals indeed could be transmitted, Congress passed a bill establishing the

Communications Satellite Corporation, a private but really public corporation which would operate under United States Government regulation to plan, produce, own, and operate a commercial satellite communications system. The corporation would be owned jointly by the public, through investment in stock, and by the nation's various common carriers in the field of communications. No single firm was to be given an edge. That policy was firm and unequivocal and it solved what might have been a serious problem. NASA was to work closely with COMSAT, providing the launch vehicles, launching them, and carrying out the tracking and data processing. COMSAT would pay NASA for these services, 60 per cent of the cost a month before the launch and the remainder a month afterward. COMSAT would pay whether or not the launch was successful and whether or not the satellite went into orbit and performed as specified.

COMSAT was set up as a closely regulated corporation, responsible to the Federal Communications Commission. Forty-two per cent of its stock was sold to common carriers. Telephone and Telegraph became the largest stockholder; second-largest was International Telephone and Telegraph. General Telephone participated. So did Electronics and Radio Corporation of America. Any small firm could buy in if it was in the business, and so could the public.

COMSAT set out to provide international communications service. In 1965 NASA launched the Early Bird satellite to open communications across the Atlantic Ocean. Then other nations saw that they might be left behind in this space business, and soon the International Telecommunications Satellite Consortium (INTELSAT) was formed, consisting eventually of more than sixty nation members. COMSAT's role was to be manager for INTELSAT, which meant that control would be in international hands, and the business operations would rest with COMSAT. Satellites were launched year after year, until five had been put up by 1967, providing communications in an area west from Pakistan to Siam, covering Europe, Africa, North America, South America, and the Pacific. Plans were made for a satellite to cover the Indian Ocean, too, and then the whole world would be linked by communications satellites.

COMSAT, AT&T, IT&T, RCA, Western Union, and other companies did continue to do business in the satellite field. The FCC granted them authority to construct earth stations at various places in order to make use of the services performed by the satellites.

But all was not always rosy, as it developed by 1968, when International Telephone & Telegraph Company began unloading its COMSAT stock, and gave up its seats on the board of directors. IT&T complained that COMSAT was selling the services of the satellites directly to foreign governments—when that was the business IT&T was in. Actually, the service was sold by INTELSAT, but COMSAT was its manager.

There was no problem with the stock. IT&T unloaded 400,000 shares in December, having sold over half a million earlier, keeping 100,000 shares as a point of re-entry if this ever seemed sensible. IT&T had done very well, too, for on the 900,000-plus shares sold it had received $57.8 million, having invested only $21 million in the beginning. The public believed in the satellite communications business.[6]

The future of satellite communications was great, but so were the problems. In the late 1960's more and more

[6] *Washington Evening Star*, December 6, 1958.

countries were gaining the capability of launching space satellites. As long as the consortium could hold things together, all was well, but if the consortium could not please its customers and its members, at some point the communications network might break, and then anybody who wanted to could start throwing hardware into space.

The space business in satellites was only beginning. American Telephone and Telegraph had not given up, for it hoped one day to put up satellites for use in the domestic telephone service of the United States, not in order to replace existing facilities, but to supplement them.

13

The Nagging Doubts or How to Beat
the Rap

When President Kennedy studied the record of NASA, and
the big North American and McDonnell contracts in particular, it became apparent that the nation was plunged into
a new kind of relationship between industry and government in the aerospace business. The relationship had begun to change as early as 1946 in the infant days of the Defense Department's missile program which had spawned
the new nonprofit private corporations in government service. RAND was the prime example, but there were a number

of others, including ANSER, an acronym for Analytic Services Inc.[1] ANSER came into being when the government decided that its relations with Corvey Engineering Company, later with its successor Melpar, were not above reproach. The solution was ANSER, a nonprofit corporation which took over the analytic studies wanted by the Air Force. Others, formed for similar reasons, were the Institute for Defense Analysis (IDA), and Space Technology Laboratories, which broke away from Thompson-Ramo-Wooldridge when conflicts were seen, and Aerospace Corporation was formed. The Army had Research Analysis Corporation, a nonprofit company organized in 1961 to do operations research, which had been done earlier by Johns Hopkins University.

One evident way to solve some of the problems was to turn to the universities as nonprofit institutions and largely above suspicion. NASA inaugurated a program in 1962 which reached its height in 1966 with the expenditure of $128 million on universities. Some of this money was spent to secure specific services. For example, nine hundred university experimenters worked with NASA's balloon, sounding rocket, and deep space and satellite programs. The University of Wisconsin took on a continuing study of meteorological problems in connection with TIROS. Some two hundred universities, representing every state in the union, became involved in NASA projects.[2] The universities worked on materials technology, flight medicine, biology, and earth resources, in some thirteen hundred projects.

[1] House Report No. 97, 88th Congress 1st Session, by the Committee on Government Operations. 13th report.
[2] Statement of Francis B. Smith, Assistant Administrator of NASA for University Affairs, before the Committee on Aeronautical and Space Sciences, U.S. Senate, 1969.

In addition to this direct program, which provided services and information that otherwise might have had to come from industry—entailing conflict of interest when a company made a study with one hand and sought the hardware contract with the other—NASA began in 1962 a sustaining university program. Part of this program was designed to train an additional one thousand Ph.D.'s each year in space science and technology. By 1969 152 universities had been given grants, and seventeen hundred persons received their doctorates directly as a result. Later, when Congress and the Bureau of the Budget objected to this shotgun approach and expenditure, NASA geared its university program down a bit, and late in the 1960's it was concentrating on the "multidisciplinary research grant." At the University of Tennessee it conducted a research program into the uses of remote sensor technology. Students of the colleges of engineering, agriculture, and the departments of botany, geography, geology, and physics cooperated with the TVA and Oak Ridge national laboratory in this program.

One important program at the University of Pennsylvania established a new philosophy of education. A research grant was given for the creation of The Institute for Direct Energy Conversion—a complicated name for a complicated idea. The rapid advances of technology were breaking down the old lines between academic disciplines. In the field of energy conversion, a man had to know a great deal outside his specialty. So this institute brought students together from various fields to work in a common laboratory on common problems. The initial staff consisted of professors of mechanical engineering, electrical engineering, metallurgical engineering, material science, and electrochemistry. They continued their normal university duties, but gave about 20 per cent of their time to this experiment in "interdisciplinary curriculum."

The first NASA grant to the Institute was given in 1962, and funds were planned for eight years, to a total of $850,000 by the end of the program in July 1970. The institute's goal was to produce four Ph.D.'s each year who would be experts in direct energy conversion. Studies were made which led to a new approach to direct energy conversion in boiling fuel cells and in techniques for forming new materials. Some ten papers per year were prepared at the institute for publication in scientific journals, and a textbook was written there for teaching solid-state energy conversion. Some graduates went into industry. One went to the University of Delaware to teach direct energy conversion—and a new discipline was born. Another went to the staff of the University of Tehran, and soon Iran became interested in development of a power system on this basis. Two business firms were formed in this field by graduates and staff members.[3]

From this program came several offshoots. One is the electric automobile study sponsored by the Department of Commerce to see if the electric car could be resuscitated usefully. The institute, the university, and General Motors Corporation joined forces to study terrestrial travel. They established an "interdisciplinary team" of experts in traffic, economics, city planning, environments, pollution, and operations research, along with the energy conversion. This team received a grant of $300,000 from the Department of Housing and Urban Development.

Other direct relationships between universities and

[3] Notes prepared for the author by Edward R. Redding of the NASA University Affairs staff.

business, stimulated by NASA, include a project carried out by the Colorado School of Mines and Martin Marietta Corporation to check the values of using remote sensors in the Bonanza mining district of Colorado. This is the use of sensors developed to give information about the physical system of space.

Universities, of course, are in constant competition with one another in a very genteel way—struggling to obtain the best and most grants. There is no bidding as such, but there is a limitation on the NASA funds. The competition comes in ideas: in the lunar landing of Apollo, the University of Maryland contributed an experiment with a laser retro-refractor. Columbia University's Lamont Laboratory put a passive seismometer aboard, with NASA's permission.[4] Other universities, not so lucky, did not have their programs approved for the flight.

Competition came in another way: NASA budgeted millions of dollars for training in public administration and management, with the realization that technology is advancing in the space business much faster than management capability. Twelve universities won awards in this field. At Syracuse, for example, students worked on organization, management relationships, and policy questions coming from a large-scale research and development program. Their studies were particularly aimed at the NASA planning and control system, an examination of the managerial and financial problems peculiar to the space business and government. In the summer of 1969 students from Syracuse worked in Washington, studying the history of NASA management. The idea was to get reports and papers clarifying policy issues, and to train administrators for government at the same

4 Statement of Francis B. Smith.

time. Similar programs were carried on at the Universities of New Mexico, Southern California, and Pittsburgh. Actually a Pittsburgh professor in the School of Public Administration had been involved in the NASA program as early as the preparation of the Kimpton report—although McKinsey officials did not feel that he contributed very much to the outcome.[5]

Finally, NASA offered grants for university research and training in engineering systems design. Five universities won out over others to train graduate engineers to work with systems that are used in the space business.

Universities, then, became an important part of the space business with the coming to NASA of James E. Webb, and their use removed some of the problems of conflict of interest that arose when government dealt with business in research and development.

But not all.

One way the old NACA-oriented men had tried to keep the uproar down was to carry on a good deal of in-house research. Industry did not much like that, and political leaders were convinced that the American system ought to be promoted by the traditional use of government to control and lead business, but not to take on the business functions. However, almost everything NASA did fell within the realm of research and development. An aerospace company could afford to spend a good deal of money (although most of it was government money) on research and development of a guided missile because hundreds or thousands of them would be produced and the company would make its profits on the assembly line. But with a program like Mercury or Apollo, every spacecraft would be hand-fabricated,

[5] Kimpton Committee work papers in NASA archives.

and each would be different from the other because the technology was advancing so rapidly in this new field of space exploration.

By the summer of 1961, President Kennedy recognized the special problems that were arising in all fields that concerned space. In fiscal 1962, for instance, the Department of Defense was spending nearly seven million dollars for research and development, and NASA was spending two and a half million dollars, with about 70 per cent of this money going to private industry. But one serious problem was the proliferation of these nonprofit companies. Industry complained bitterly that if the nonprofit participants continued to expand, they were simply taking money out of the hands of the space business.

President Kennedy responded to these complaints by appointing a committee headed by David E. Bell, director of the Bureau of the Budget, to investigate and make some recommendations. The committee was thenceforth known as the Bell committee. It included Secretary of Defense Robert McNamara; chairman of the Atomic Energy Commission Glenn Seaborg; administrator Webb; Dr. Alan T. Waterman, director of the National Science Foundation; Dr. Jerome B. Wiesner, scientific adviser to President Kennedy; and chairman John W. Macy, Jr., of the Civil Service Commission.

The Bell report recommended that government agencies raise salaries in order to keep competent people in management positions, and that procurement machinery be improved and quality performance emphasized in relations with business. From this came several actions. Most important was the formation of a new group within NASA to make a procurement study and the employment of an outside firm, Harbridge House, to help.[6]

From this study developed the incentive contract: a contractor could take on a NASA project with a series of goals and conditions that would determine his rewards for the work. If he met the goals or passed them, he might make a considerable amount of money from the project. If he did a sloppy job, he might not make anything. The selection of contractors would continue to be a problem, but, as set up now by administrator Webb, not only the business firm's proposal but also its "intrinsic competence" were to be crucial factors. A complex system was then established to manage contracts. In other words, a contractor who went into business with NASA would find government men looking over his shoulder all the way.

The complexity of such intensive management and the management capability gap in the space business are both indicated by what happened next, as told by Robert L. Rosholt in his official *Administrative History of NASA 1958–1963*:

> An early and significant managerial innovation in NASA's manned space flight program following the November 1961 reorganization was the establishment in December 1961 of a management council to coordinate the manned space flight program. The council was chaired by [D. Brainerd] Holmes [head of the manned space flight program] and was initially composed of the top two officials of the two manned space flight centers [Marshall and Manned Spacecraft] and Holmes' five principal subordinates in Headquarters. Regular monthly meetings were held. When the council was formed, the two field centers were not

[6] Rosholt, pp. 270 *et seq.*

under Holmes' line of command, but rather were under Associate Administrator Seamans. Holmes sought to use the council as a means of arriving at a unanimous position on major matters without having to worry whether the action was within his rather complete program authority or not. According to Holmes, the council was to "spot and identify problems as early as possible and to resolve them quickly."

The council was not able to solve all problems, however. Because Von Braun [director of Marshall Center] and Gilruth [director of Manned Spacecraft Center] held equal status with Holmes in NASA's organizational hierarchy, they had the theoretical ability to go over his head. . . . This situation was changed in October 1962, by giving Holmes another hat at the Deputy Associate Administrator's level. This move created a better decision-making environment. . . .

It also created more government. More committees—committee after committee.

Another, very important result of the Bell report was the strengthening of an old policy. The people in the space business did not like the idea of government subsidizing nonprofit corporations that paid high salaries to individuals and competed against the business firms in every way. But if the nonprofit corporations were to be held down, and if the government was to refrain from setting up its own fabrication plants, then business would have to give a little here and there. The solution was to call on business firms to undertake some management tasks—and thereby give up their chances to compete for hardware contracts.

One such contract was that made by the government with General Electric Corporation in February 1962 for integration and checking on the Apollo space vehicle and its systems. It was a big contract—GE would get $30 million in 1963 and $100 million in 1964. In return for this contract, GE agreed not to seek any contracts for Apollo hardware, or anything to do with Apollo where the company's information about North American's efforts could be used to GE's advantage. If there were any place in the program where GE's special abilities might be of use to the government, then the administrator or his deputy would decide. (GE also held a government contract to operate the Mississippi Test facility of the George C. Marshall Space Flight Center, for which the company received a fee of $114,500.)[7] At the end of project Apollo, when GE had performed the work and collected the estimated $635 million for the service, GE could then compete for anything. The government was paying that much to General Electric to assure that nothing went wrong with Apollo. GE's response was to withdraw from the bidding for the lunar excursion module, which went to Grumman.

At about the same time, NASA made another contract for special services, to solve a different problem. NASA had established a systems engineering office as part of the manned space flight program, but it was very quickly apparent that this office would not be able to handle the job of supervising. The problem was that government simply did not pay enough to attract the men qualified to get the task done on schedule. In February 1962, administrator Webb wrote to the president of American Telephone and Telegraph, asking him to provide these services of systems analysis and engineering.[8] He indicated the restrictions that would be placed on the Bell system because the company

[7] House report no. 917, November 22, 1963. Thirteenth report by the committee on Government Operations.
[8] Rosholt, pp. 274–275.

would have unique knowledge of NASA plans and activities. President E. J. McNeely replied that AT&T would get up a separate subsidiary corporation within the Bell System to do the job for the government, as Webb had suggested. The Bell system borrowed people from Bell Laboratories, Western Electric, and other companies in the system and established Bellcomm, which set up its headquarters in Washington.

Bellcomm would help NASA make the systems specifications for the manned space flight program. It would study the problems of launch from the surface of the moon and check out the systems that were developed. It would help prepare the reliability program for the Apollo project, putting together the analytical and technical work of the various space centers and doing part of that work itself. It could do what NASA could not do, and do it quickly, because it had the skilled people. Salaries were high, compared to government pay: twenty-one Bellcomm employees earned more than $20,000 a year and four earned more than $30,000.[9]

Like General Electric, the Bell system was then precluded from seeking other NASA work except what might be considered its normal communications services. In the first eighteen months the company received $8.5 million, and in 1964 it was paid $12.7 million.

The importance of this concept developed by administrator Webb was that it resolved some of the difficulties between government and industry that had been plaguing the space business since the establishment of RAND. Space businessmen could not complain about the formation of "phony" corporations which they regarded as setups to

9 Rosholt, p. 276.

give higher pay than government normally allowed. The difficulty was that in creating the new relationship between government and big business, government yielded control responsibilities to industry. The ultimate result of this no one could predict.

14

The Apollo Disaster

By 1963 the complications of the American space effort were so great as to make the program incomprehensible to the general public. Even the specialists found that they were not keeping abreast of activity among their co-workers on other projects. To some extent this problem had been attacked by a reorganization of NASA in 1961, but administrator Webb wanted the lines of authority clearer yet, so he reorganized NASA again in 1963. He divided NASA activity into three basic programs: Manned Space Flight, Space Science and Applications, and Advanced Research and

Technology. Most important, of course, in the public thinking, was the manned space flight program that was to put a man on the moon not later than 1970. Even by 1963, and with an estimated $40 billion to spend, the space men were getting a little worried about the nation's ability to do the job in time. There was a feeling of tension and almost frustration in the organization, and this reorganization was partly designed to reassure the space workers and the public that the job could be done.[1]

To understand the Apollo project and its problems, it must be remembered that President Kennedy had campaigned by attacking the Eisenhower space program, then had put America in the moon race in 1961. In July of that year the first industry conference on Apollo was held. A month later NASA briefed various aircraft manufacturing firms on the needs of the program. In September several big firms were invited to bid on it. In October five business firms submitted proposals for the development of the Apollo spacecraft. It came down to a contest among McDonnell Aircraft which had built the Mercury ships, Martin Aircraft, and North American Aviation Incorporated. And then, for economic reasons, it came down to Martin, with a bid of about six hundred million dollars, and North American, with a bid of about four hundred million dollars. This situation created a serious problem because many of the experts in NASA were certain that McDonnell was most capable, and that Martin was far more capable of building the spacecraft than North American Aviation. But in the end money

[1] Robert L. Rosholt, *An Administrative History of NASA, 1958–1968*, National Aeronautics and Space Administration, 1966, p. 298. Rosholt says: "Since the manned lunar landing tended to permeate, and in fact was designed to animate, almost everything NASA did, it is extremely difficult to appraise changes in the rest of NASA's program."

talked, and NASA officials were persuaded that North American was perfectly competent to undertake the development of the new spacecraft, even if inexperienced in the field.[2]

So the work began. But from the beginning it was a confused program: NASA had made some miscalculations, and the bidding figures ceased to mean anything. What had been requested was a Nova vehicle, a new design with an entirely different system of operation. But the scientists discovered that by increasing the capability of the Saturn V rocket, and by using the lunar-orbit rendezvous system of reaching the moon area, the building of an entirely new design could be obviated. So although North American had the contract plum, all the old specifications were thrown out.[3]

What had been a plan became, financially at least, a patchwork. And by 1965 the Apollo program was in serious difficulty, so much so that General Samuel Phillips, Apollo program director, began to take a long hard look at the way the Apollo space capsule was shaping up. That autumn he was definitely dismayed with sloppy workmanship, high expense, and bad scheduling. The Apollo program was on the way to costing three times as much as North American Aviation had bid, if the projections could be believed, and the job was not being done right.

". . . The rate of solution of technical problems, the ability to comply with our program requirements in terms of schedules, to be able to conduct the business in accordance with the cost estimate was creating a considerable problem

---

[2] Hearings before the Subcommittee on NASA Oversight of the Committee on Science and Astronautics, U.S. House of Representatives, Ninetieth Congress, first session, Vol. 1. p. 553.
[3] *Ibid.*

for me in keeping the total program in balance," said the general.[4]

General Phillips then called his assistants around him, including Dr. George Mueller, associate administrator, and sent a task force to California to investigate conditions at North American Aviation. The task force spent several days at the company plant and headquarters, studying the planning, operations, and products that were being made by North American and the twenty thousand subcontractors who had a hand in some part of the Apollo program.

Phillips's associates returned to Washington in a fine state of worry. In meetings held in December 1965 there was even talk of abandoning North American as the prime contractor. Obviously, however, that would mean starting all over again, and with the 1970 target date set by the Kennedy Administration, it just would not do to lose more than four years of work time. Certainly something could be salvaged, and starting over altogether in 1965 was something that no one connected with the space program was prepared to face.

North American was frantic, for to lose the Apollo contract at this time might easily bring about collapse of the company—it certainly would put it out of the space business for the foreseeable future. North American promised every possible degree of cooperation with the NASA authorities in improving the planning, cutting the costs, and taking closer supervision of the quality of the products to go into the spacecraft.

Following the December meetings in Washington, General Phillips made strong specific verbal recommendations and presented informal notes of his findings to the com-

[4] *Hearings*, p. 379.

pany. The jumpy officials of North American lost no time in attempting to comply, working on those items listed.

General Phillips's watchfulness continued into the spring of 1966. He and other senior officers of NASA again traveled to the North American plant and observed carefully the caliber of work going on there. Again the NASA officials met to discuss their findings. Someone proposed that some of the work North American was not doing well be taken over by NASA itself. But North American resisted such change, for it was committed to employment of some thirty-five thousand persons on this project, plus another twenty-five thousand persons employed by various subcontractors who provided integral parts and supplies to North American. The complication of change was obviously to be avoided if possible.

In the months between December 1965 and April 1967, North American made frantic efforts to comply with the NASA demands, and by April 22, 1966, when General Phillips and Dr. Mueller saw J. L. Atwood, president and chairman of North American, many of the problems had been met, and the NASA officials could at least hope that North American would perform in a proficient fashion. The general had personally given Atwood those notes about the deficiencies he had discovered, and four months later he felt that North American had made good progress in achieving necessary changes. He dropped his idea of turning some of the manufacturing of components over to NASA's own shops and North American went ahead.[5]

So the work continued. Spacecraft 012 was begun and assigned to Mission AS-204. Building which had started in August 1964 at the North American plant in Downey, Cali-

[5] *Hearings* (General Phillips's testimony), pp. 384–399.

fornia, was not really interrupted by the complaints of 1965 and 1966. The structure was ready in 1965, and the installation of the complicated subsystems began, layer upon layer. Following the complaints by General Phillips and his staff, the designs and workmanship were thoroughly reviewed at Downey in February and March.

All the subsystems were checked. In July and August 1965, NASA and North American officials went over the spacecraft carefully, item by item. In all this, from the designing to this 'customer acceptance readiness review,' the astronauts were consulted, and each complaint or suggestion that any of them had to make was taken very seriously. It had to be, for in the final analysis it was the lives of the astronauts which were at stake, and under the NASA scheme no astronaut had to step into a capsule if he believed it was unsafe to fly.

So the work went on, and along with it the constant revision of items and subsystems that was necessary in this new field where the space "experts" had only the limited experience of less than a decade on which to depend.

In August, NASA issued North American a Certificate of Flight Worthiness for Spacecraft 012. That certificate did not mean the spacecraft was ready for blast-off—far from it. What it did mean was that the spacecraft was far enough along in construction to be shipped to Cape Kennedy, and that the remainder of the work could be done there. There were hundreds of items that must be corrected before the spacecraft would be ready for flight. The total number of needed changes was not even known at the time of shipment, but that was not unusual.

The part of the spacecraft in which the astronauts would ride, known as the command module, was received at Kennedy Space Center on August 26, 1966. There it was connected to the "service module," which contained much of the working mechanism.

The work continued.

In September and October, literally hundreds of changes were made in parts of the spacecraft. New parts and materials were ordered from North American and sometimes from the NASA facilities. They were installed and tested. The astronauts came and went, looking over the shoulders of the builders and engineers. No one expected the spacecraft to be perfect at this point and, indeed, no one would have known perfection had they seen it, for the space workers were feeling their way.

Dr. Mueller and his assistants came to the Kennedy Space Center and went over the capsule, consulting with the scientists, engineers, and astronauts. The North American engineers stood by until these NASA officials completed this final basic inspection and issued a Design Certification Document on October 7, 1966. Still there were hundreds of items to be corrected, but it was the way of the space program, harried as it was by a feeling of hurry, that conditional approvals be given at every step save the last—that of blast-off. This was the approach of the space business from the beginning, and there was no change during the Apollo program. It represented basic American business philosophy—even as the design of spacecraft known as Block K was preparing to go into space, scientists and engineers were working on a better space capsule, known as Block II. But the pressures were such that it was not feasible to abandon the Block K craft if the schedule of the Apollo program was to be met, *i.e.*, if Americans were to put a man on the moon by 1970.[6]

[6] Report of Apollo Review Board to the Administrator, National Aeronautics and Space Administration, p. 4–2.

On October 10, the flight crews of Apollo 204 assembled to begin the first manned tests. Astronauts Virgil I. Grissom, Edward H. White, and Roger B. Chaffee came to take these tests, along with the backup team headed by astronaut Walter Schirra. Deficiencies were quickly discovered, and the test was discontinued on October 11 while parts (bent umbilical pins) were changed. Next day the test was begun again and it was completed on October 13. For the two following days apparently satisfactory unmanned tests were run.

Then problems began to develop.

On October 18 a manned simulated flight test was begun. Then a transistor in an inverter broke down; the test was held up and finished the next day. Two days later Walter Schirra's backup crew began a simulated altitude test, using a complete oxygen atmosphere. An oxygen system regulator failed and the test was held up. NASA engineers studied the part and found that it had to be redesigned, so it was sent back to North American for the work.[7]

While this part was being remade work continued on the spacecraft. It had come to Kennedy Space Center with hundreds of design-change orders, and each day new parts arrived to be installed. NASA and North American worked around the clock—in three shifts—to keep the manned flight program going and try to make the target dates.

Late in October the whole environmental control unit—the oxygen system—was removed from the spacecraft and sent back to the North American factory at Downey for design changes. There were leakages in the evaporator in the water glycol system that would protect the men from intense heat on escape from and re-entry into the earth's atmosphere.

[7] *Ibid.*, p. 4–1.

At about this time astronaut Gus Grissom and the others began talking about the "lemon" they had to work with, and Grissom even hung a lemon inside the spacecraft in jest, to give his fellow workers both a laugh and an indication of some of the astronauts' feelings. There was nothing very definable about it, and Grissom and the others knew that in the final analysis *they* were the ones who would make the decisions as to the safety of the spacecraft.

So far, the tests the astronauts were conducting were regarded as non-hazardous. The astronauts did not like to see so many *parts* needing redesign, but this was a *part* of the game. Gus Grissom's wry comment was to the effect that he was uneasy about sitting on top of a firecracker inside a spacecraft with ten thousand moving parts—each of them made by the firm that submitted the lowest bid.[8]

In the next few weeks there were many changes. Most troublesome was the environmental control system, whose plumbing continued to leak. This plumbing had been made of aluminum piping, because weight was a big factor, and when things were moved about in the spacecraft, and the unit put in and out, there was a tendency to strain the welding at the joints. In any event, it leaked, and it was not until December 14 that it was sent back for repairs.

Altogether, the plumbing was to leak six *known* times inside the spacecraft, fluid falling on the plating and on wires covered with lightweight teflon. This was to become important because the water glycol was corrosive and also the residue when dry was highly combustible.[9]

The changes seemed to be interminable—which meant that workmen were swarming about inside the space-

[8] Burt English, of National Aerospace Industries of America, to author, November 1968.
[9] Report of Apollo Review Board, p. 4–2.

craft removing one item and replacing another. In order to go in and out, the workmen had to take off their shoes and put on padded sock-like booties, the purpose being to keep them from scuffing the tender teflon coating of the wires, or bumping other interior working parts of the spacecraft.

Just after Christmas, the spacecraft was moved back into the altitude chamber and testing was resumed. On December 29 and 30 Walter Schirra and the backup crew made the manned altitude test, using oxygen in the cabin and in their suits.

Everything seemed to be fine. Here is how NASA put it:

"It should be noted that this final manned test in the altitude chamber was very successful with all spacecraft systems functioning normally. At the post-test debriefing the backup flight crew expressed their satisfaction with the condition and performance of the spacecraft.

"It should also be noted that in the altitude chamber tests the Command Module was pressurized with pure oxygen four times at pressure greater than 14.7 psia for a total time of six hours and 15 minutes." The total time was about two-and-a-half times longer than the time that it would be under such pressure during the actual preflight test on the pad.

So everyone was satisfied.

Or nearly everyone.

One who was dissatisfied, and intensely so, was a disgruntled employee of North American Aviation named Thomas Ronald Baron, a missile preflight inspector. Baron was so upset with the performance of his company that in the autumn of 1965 he began keeping notes of what in his mind were failures by North American Aviation to live up to the specifications laid down by government. By November, Baron was suffering from an ulcer, which exaggerated a general condition of precarious health established by diabetes, and was in the hospital. He was a worrier and a worried man, and part of the month of December he was in the hospital.

One particular reason he was worried is that he had worked for a time on the water/glycol system, and had gone through some of the troubles in the installation and checking of that system.

Baron spent much time talking to other space employees of NASA and North American about deficiencies in the program, and he went home at night and wrote up his notes. He spoke of "noncertified" items—unaccepted items—which were actually installed in the spacecraft and about which nothing could be done: paints, epoxy materials, and tape. He spoke of breakdowns in communications on the pad, where men working with fuels worked under dangerous conditions for a long period of time. The men on the scene complained, but nothing was done.

He spoke of bad morale among North American employees, and he named the men who had left the company and the program. He described specific instances of danger, and gave names. He told how he, not an engineer, was left in charge of verifying proper installation of components in the spacecraft—a responsibility he did not feel he should have.

He spoke of overwork and fifty-five and sixty hours a week spent on the job. He told of one occasion on which a fifty-five-gallon drum of 190-proof alcohol was delivered to the launch site, the alcohol to be used to clean out the environmental control unit. One man took a five-gallon jug of the alcohol home with him. He and others put more alcohol into plastic bags, cut it with water, and began drinking on the job.

Baron spoke of repairs being made without reports or written controls of the work. All this material went into reports to North American over a period of a year.[10]

The testing went on.

On January 6, 1967, the spacecraft was mated to the launch rockets at Launch Complex 34, which meant the mission was coming very close to the countdown stage. Yet others, as well as Baron, were worried because so many changes had to be made.

As NASA put it:

> The effort and rework required on Spacecraft 012 at KSC was greater than that experienced on the first manned Gemini spacecraft. However, since the Apollo spacecraft was considerably more complex than Gemini spacecraft, this does not necessarily indicate that the quantity of problems encountered was excessive. There is, however, an inference that the design, qualification and fabrication process may not have been completed adequately prior to shipment to KSC.[11]

Most of that work was completed by January 27, 1967. On that day the astronauts Grissom, White, and Chaffee entered the spacecraft to make one of the final tests before launching, a test called the Space Vehicle Plugs Out Integrated Test, which was to check all space vehicle systems and working procedures. By that time only four known deficiencies had not been corrected. It was decided by the NASA officials that the test could be made without those

[10] Hearings, House of Representatives, Vol. 1, pp. 483–500.
[11] Report of Apollo Review Board, p. 4–2.

corrections because the January 27 test was not supposed to be dangerous.

North American had written the standards for the test. The astronauts insisted on one extra precaution at this time: a test of the emergency escape system. They were to simulate an emergency at the end of the test and then practice getting out of the spacecraft as quickly as possible.

So the Plugs Out Test began January 27. The astronauts climbed into their space suits and went to the pad, rode up the elevator in the gantry, and entered the space capsule at 1300 Eastern Standard Time. Almost immediately Grissom noted a bad smell in the spacecraft, and spoke out. The count was held at 1320 and the odor was investigated; the cause of it was sought, but not found at the time. Still the smell was eliminated and an hour and twenty minutes later the countdown was resumed. Three hours later came more trouble, this time with the communications system—a continuously live microphone that could not be turned off inside the spacecraft. Then came more communications problems: some of the ground personnel could not hear each other or the spacecraft crew. So at 1820 the count was held at T-10, and all concerned tried to solve the communications problem from the outside.

For ten minutes nothing was heard from inside the spacecraft.

Then came 1830.

The pulse and respiratory counters of the three astronauts indicated that they were doing virtually nothing inside the spacecraft, lying on their couches and resting, waiting for the test to be resumed.

Thirty seconds later the electrical equipment recorded a short circuit in the system inside the space capsule.

A few seconds afterwards came the cry:

"Fire in the spacecraft."

The procedure inside the spacecraft called for astronaut White, who occupied the center couch, to unlatch the hatch. Witnesses watching the command module hatch window on television saw that he was apparently trying to do so.

North American's Donald O. Babbitt was stationed at the pad leader's desk in the gantry not far from the command module. He heard what he thought was Chaffee's voice announcing the fire, and then—seconds later—was nearly blasted by a sheet of flame that struck the desk and charred both desk and the papers on it. He fled to the area called the White Room, next door, and there saw three mechanics and another worker who had a headset. He told the man with the headset to notify the test supervisor of the fire, and send firemen, ambulances, and equipment. Then he grabbed a carbon dioxide fire extinguisher and ran back toward the capsule.

Other men of North American and NASA came up with extinguishers and tried to put out the fire, which was burning in the capsule. In a few moments it was all over. Working in the dense smoke, Babbitt and the others managed to get the hatches off the spacecraft and get the astronauts out.

There were three hatches. The men opened the first hatch, were overcome by smoke, passed their tools to others, and went gasping out of the White Room. The second hatch was opened more easily.

The third or inner hatch was unlatched, and, although the workers could not get it clear entirely from outside, they managed to push it open three-quarters of the way.

Out came a dense cloud of smoke accompanied by intense heat.

In five minutes it was all over. Pad leader Babbitt went out of the White Room, put on a headset, and informed the blockhouse that the astronauts seemed to be dead and the fire had burned itself out.

Immediately, then, the investigative procedure was put into effect. All outgoing calls were stopped. Personnel were warned not to talk to anyone other than investigators. The area was sealed in effect, so the experts could examine the capsule in detail and ascertain what had gone wrong.

The investigation occupied many weeks, and thousands of man hours. For example, some five thousand pictures of the interior and exterior of the space capsule was taken, as the investigators stripped away the residue of what had been the controls and equipment before the fire, in an effort to discover what had caused the disaster.[12]

As always, hindsight was much clearer than the view at the time of the events. Dr. Floyd L. Thompson, chairman of the review board, noted at the end of the investigation that there had been far too much flammable material in the spacecraft. There had been a very definite risk of fire, from the beginning. Indeed, back in the days of the Gemini program a similar fire had been staged in testing a spacecraft under the same general conditions. But this had been forgotten, or laid aside in memory because nobody really expected a fire.

The investigators discovered that the astronauts had tried to get out but could not open the hatch from the inside because of the air pressure. Then, when fire ruptured

[12] Results of the special investigation by NASA filled some 2,700 pages of report before it was finished.

the airtight command module, it was too late; their oxygen supply had burned up, and they died. It was discovered that it took too long *in any event* for the men to get out of the capsule. In other words, the capsule was a trap in case of fire.

Also important, the investigators found that the people responsible for the planning, conduct, and safety of the test simply did not see that it would be a hazardous undertaking, so no preparations for an emergency were made.

There were, in all, eleven findings. Who could say which were most serious? Fault could be found in many areas, and perhaps it could be said that the astronauts themselves were responsible for their deaths because they went into a capsule that did not meet the safety requirements it ought to have met. Or one could say that the Kennedy Administration was responsible for setting up the goal of a man on the moon by 1970, or the Johnson Administration, for continuing to press that program. The question was raised: can one properly set timetables in a technology that depends on science and the development of the unknown?

But as far as the space business is concerned, the investigation brought out several important points. Finding No. 10 of the review board was particularly damning to North American Aviation:

> *Deficiencies existed in Command Module design, workmanship, and quality control, such as:*
>
> *a. Components of the Environmental Control System installed in Command Module 012 had a history of many removals and of technical difficulties, including regulator failures, line failures and Environmental Control Unit failures. The design and installation features of the Environmental Control Unit makes removal or repair difficult.*

b. Coolant leakage at solder joints had been a chronic problem.

c. The coolant is both corrosive and combustible.

d. Deficiencies in design, manufacture, installation rework and quality control existed in the electrical wiring.

e. No vibration test was made of a complete flight-configured spacecraft.

f. Spacecraft design and operating procedures currently require the disconnecting of electrical connections while powered.

g. No design features for fire protection were incorporated.[13]

Finding 11 was almost as grave an indictment of the manufacturer and the NASA authorities who allowed the spacecraft to be brought to Kennedy Space Center with so many known deficiencies. Here, too, was the indictment of the pressure under which the Apollo program was operating, pressure to meet target dates so that the program could stay on the track. Compared to the purely scientific programs, the pace and pressure were disgraceful and dangerous: in 1967 ten out of ten satellites launched were launched successfully, including Explorer and Pioneer vehicles for the study of solar wind, cosmic rays, and other phenomena in deep space, and the Mariner V which made a close fly-by of Venus.[14] An indication of the pace of the scientific work was given in the Johnson Administration's announcement about the Mariner space satellite studies of the future: "Two Mariner spacecraft are to be launched *around* March, 1969," to be sent to fly by Mars and collect data about that mysterious planet. But if they were not ready

---

[13] Report of Apollo 204 Review Board, p. 6–3.
[14] *Aerospace Facts and Figures, 1968*, published by Aerospace Industries Association of America.

in March, the pressures to launch would not be overly severe, as they are in the Apollo manned flight program—a program which some prominent scientists believe to be dangerous, foolish, and premature.[15]

The findings and recommendations of the Apollo review board did not end the study of the accident on Pad 34 at Kennedy Space Center. Both the United States Senate and the House of Representatives conducted their own investigations into the accident, which they called the "NASA oversight." The hearings came in the spring of 1967, and although they did not lead to any immediate action on the part of Congress, they did bring up interesting questions about the space business. In the initial excitement over the accident, NASA tried to stop contractors and government employees from saying anything at all, from talking to press or public about the affair. This nervous reaction proved to be neither wise nor helpful in the cause of determining the facts, and the order for silence was wisely rescinded from Washington very shortly after it was laid down.[16]

The Congressional hearings brought out a number of new points about the accident, not least of which was the growing awareness of the astronauts that they had been protected by less than an optimum safety program under the system devised by NASA and North American. Astronaut Frank Borman so testified.[17] Again it seemed that the fault lay not so much with individuals as with the general atmosphere of hurry-hurry that prevailed in the Apollo program before the accident. Admittedly, NASA was responsible for the safety of the astronauts, NASA had re-

[15] Sir Bernard Torell, *The New York Times*, November 25, 1968.
[16] Testimony of James Webb before House Committee, Hearings, Vol. 1, pp. 55–56.
[17] Testimony of Col. Frank Borman, House Committee Hearings, Vol. 1, pp. 77–101.

peatedly brought to the attention of the officials of North American instances of near-negligence on the manufacturer's part. Of course not all of the deficiencies were the result of North American's own workmanship, but North American assumed the responsibility for checking the work of its thousands of subcontractors.

A side issue not developed in the hearings is: could any manufacturing concern be expected to take so much responsibility? For example, the spacecraft contained some twenty miles of electrical wiring, protected by a teflon coating. The wiring literally threaded through the entire spacecraft. Who was to say that at some time in installation, or in working in the craft, parts of the covering had not been destroyed? Who indeed was to check such detail, when it was established that by January 1967 development had come so far that certain lower strata of the spacecraft were virtually inaccessible? It was known that the wiring was not all it should be; five instances of electrical arcing had been reported. But the remedy was something else again, and part of the problem was suggested by the finding of a workman's wrench in the interior of Spacecraft 012 after the fire.

North American had its problems. One of the most serious was a heavy turnover of employees, mentioned by President Atwood in his testimony before the board. The reason for the turnover could be found in the roots of the affluent and intensely mobile society of the 1960's. In addition to giving pay raises and promotions, North American had conducted several personnel programs to try to keep the people working on the Apollo committed to their responsibilities. One of these was called PRIDE—Personal Responsibility in Daily Effort.[18]

[18] Testimony of J. L. Atwood, President, North American Aviation, House Committee Hearings, Vol. 1, p. 143.

How well did these work?

Not so very well, if the testimony of Thomas Baron could be accepted. Baron had begun his note-taking in 1965, and a year later he was thoroughly dispirited and disgusted with North American's methods. His own morale was very low, complicated by his poor health, and he attributed the same low state of morale to many of the North American employees at Cape Kennedy. Baron discussed the deficiencies of North American's program with NASA investigator John Brooks. He also compiled a brief fifty-page report, several hours of tape discussion of deficiencies in the Apollo program, and a five hundred-page report on troublesome matters at Kennedy Space Center. At the end of 1966 Baron's employment with North American was terminated, which, of course, did not make him any friendlier to the management. When the members of the House subcommittee appeared at Kennedy Space Center on April 21 to take testimony, Baron appeared. Earlier he had submitted his various reports to House members, and responsible officials of NASA had indicated that while they believed there was much exaggeration in Baron's statements, there was also a good deal of truth in his contention that sloppy workmanship had bedeviled the Apollo program.

Baron's testimony was not very conclusive. He named more than a dozen persons who he said could corroborate various parts of his five-hundred-page memorandum on conditions in the Apollo program. Some of the committee members had read at least parts of his report. They were pulled two ways, and Baron's case took a decided turn for the worse when North American officials produced one employee, Al Holmburg, who proved either frightened or totally taciturn, and confirmed nothing at all in Baron's statements.

Actually, the Congressional investigating committees were well within their right and responsibility in leaving the investigation where they did. Their announced area of investigation was the accident itself. In reply to direct questioning, administrator Webb, an accomplished speaker, made the case for the manner in which the total NASA program had been conducted. Committee members were wondering if McDonnell Aircraft Company could not have done a better job of putting the space capsule together than North American was doing. Webb was ready for the question with as complete an answer as he could formulate.

> . . . The present contractor, North American Aviation, was selected as a result of this procurement action with a Source Evaluation Board that had a very great deal of help and had done its work carefully.
>
> Dr. Gilruth was responsible for the Source Evaluation Board; Dr. Dryden, Dr. Seamans and I were unanimous in the selection of the contractor. I think it is fair to say that the Apollo system is very much more complete than anything we have had.
>
> Some people say from ten to twenty times more complex. I think it is difficult to speculate that a contractor who had a piece of equipment to fly in near earth's orbit and could take a good deal of the plumbing out of the spacecraft and put it in an adaptor section that would never have to re-enter the earth could have done a better job. His task must be compared with the Apollo which must re-enter the earth at very much higher energy dissipation rates with all of the other equipment intact inside the capsule. I think there is no evidence to support those statements today. The fact is that the people who are looking at the equipment at the Cape now and making what I regard in many cases as irresponsible criticisms of it are looking at equipment that was designed not only to fly with three men in the cockpit.

It also carries all the other equipment necessary to replace the three men so that we can test the Saturn V booster by sending this equipment out at a high altitude and driving it out in the earth; as we test the heat shield. This is a difficult operation. A great deal of the equipment is put in by what some member of the committee called this afternoon 'handwork'—it doesn't look like a production model of something where you are going to make some ten thousand items. The test results have indicated that the equipment was ready to do its job. I think that all of us who are very anxious to have complete confidence in this equipment when we have to make the decision to push the button and let these rockets fly will have again gone over this matter with the very greatest of care.

Second I would like to point out that as we have to learn to develop equipment where there was no design but where the contractor and NASA had to go through the learning process. We had evolved a Block II design which takes into account many things that are criticized by this board. In fact most of them that are important. I think you could consider Gemini made by McDonnell as a Block II Mercury made by the same company. We are going through a developmental problem on a very much larger and more complex and difficult system. I wouldn't want to leave you with the impression that I or anyone in the position of responsibility at NASA are satisfied with the work that we have done in NASA through our contracts with McDonnell or North American or the others. Every Gemini flight that we flew as successful as they were, involved difficulties and troubles. I may say we had a good deal of very deep concern in the emergency recovery of those who made the first linkup and had to come down 500 miles off Japan because of a thruster that was not in good shape. So I would say that you not go back to 1961 if you expect to get ahead of the Russians or get near to them. . . .[19]

[19] House Committee Hearings, Vol. 1, pp. 114–115.

There was the NASA argument, and if one accepted the premise that the time-honored business system of competitive bidding was the best way to handle the space program, then there could be no argument with administrator Webb.

Officials of the Aerospace Industries Association said much the same thing. One remarked that the Russians were in exactly the same situation with their space program, although they might call their prime contractors and subcontractors by different names.[20] And yet the nagging doubt persisted. Were there not enough questions raised, by astronaut Gus Grissom in his joking, by space worker Thomas Baron in his questioning, by NASA's own special board investigating the Apollo accident? Did not the whole space business invite reconsideration of the manner in which it was conducted in the 1960's?

[20] Burt English to author, November 1968.

15

The Complexities of the Space Business
or A Cure for Space Fever

The Apollo disaster proved one fact that responsible and thoughtful officials of NASA had known for a long time—that some day, no matter what the precautions, the inevitable faults of human nature would bring about disaster. In a situation where the failure of any one of several hundred thousand parts might create the conditions of disaster, the Apollo fire was not too surprising.

What was more surprising was the failure of the General Electric support program in the Apollo fire incident. NASA had contracted with GE for a safeguard program and had committed more than six hundred million dollars to that purpose. Yet it seems that GE did not ever actually check physical evidence, but relied on reports submitted by the other contractors to Washington. In fact, North American did not even see these reports in the form in which GE submitted them to NASA, as was indicated in the hearings before the United States Senate committee when committee members questioned NASA officials about GE's last report on the spacecraft before the fire:

THE CHAIRMAN (Senator Anderson): We have the report here Senator Holland. It states it was prepared from NASA and North American Company documents.

SENATOR HOLLAND: Mr. Chairman, I understood that we had it. I undestood that NASA had it. But I also understood, both heretofore and from what has been stated by the witness today, that there was an internal report of General Electric to NASA.

THE CHAIRMAN: What happened in the meantime? Wasn't it prepared a long time ago?

MR. MEYERS: It is my understanding it is dated December 31— April 3—excuse me.
The report is dated April 3 of this year and apparently it is a quarterly report. But it is made up of data we already had available within our own corrective action system.

THE CHAIRMAN: Is it true that the report is dated April 3, 1967, and it was not made available to your company until yesterday?

MR. MEYERS: That is my understanding.

THE CHAIRMAN: You say it is an understanding. Is there somebody who knows whether it was or was not? What about the company?
Does the company know whether it was or was not available?

MR. MEYERS: We obtained the report from the NASA KSC personnel in the last forty-eight hours.

THE CHAIRMAN: This report was prepared some time ago, it is dated April 3. It is an internal report as far as NASA is concerned. But should not the report have been sent to you at the time it was prepared?

MR. ATWOOD: Mr. Chairman, may I see if I cannot explain?

THE CHAIRMAN: It sounds like a very mystifying situation. If I was to say to a member of this staff, "Please give me certain documents," and a month later he said they are internal documents, I would say "What about it?"

MR. ATWOOD: General Electric's duty is apparently to compile this report from data obtained from the contractors at the Cape. We were one of those contractors and they took our inspection data and wrote the report. The words and comments are theirs. The data on which the report is based are ours.

I believe that is the basis of the report. When it goes to NASA distribution center, we would then receive from NASA appropriate extracts for our comment. And as Mr. Myers pointed out, some of the comments would go to other contractors, because they provided the equipment.[1]

There was the rub. Throughout its existence, NASA had gone to great lengths to protect its contractors' competitive positions, and here was a result of it. The General Electric reports would most certainly have been more effective if they had been handed directly to North American, the prime contractor on the Apollo program. For example, the General Electric report in question stated: "The cause of these discrepancies was identified as workmanship." Strong words, but not the words that reached North American when filtered through NASA, and in the case of subassem-

[1] Hearings Before the Committee on Aeronautical and Space Sciences, United States Senate, 90th Congress, Apollo Accident Part 5, May 4, 1967, pp. 410–411.

blies, the criticism of poor workmanship might not reach the prime contractor at all, because of NASA's protective policy.

The Apollo fire had many results. One of them was a complete revamping and enlargement of the safety program. Its effectiveness would be demonstrated in the successful moon landing of Apollo 11. The effect of the disaster on North American and other space contractors was, of course, electric. Quality control programs snapped suddenly to life. If Thomas Baron could state that the general level of safety and control on the site at Cape Kennedy was low at the time of the fire, this certainly could not be said thereafter.

As for North American, the company suffered for its misdeeds, whatever they may have been. One of the first actions of administrator Webb was the establishment of an office of Special Contracts Negotiation and Review, to which assistant administrator Bernard Moritz was appointed. With four assistants, Moritz set about the renegotiation of the North American contract.

Originally, the contract had called for costs plus a fixed fee for North American. In October 1965, however, NASA had decided to convert the contract to an incentive program, in order to speed the work and obtain better quality. After the fire the whole question was reopened. Obviously North American was not going to earn any incentive fees on the Apollo 7 capsule. In the agreement that followed, the contract was scaled down, and North American agreed to take less profit than it had been getting. The renegotiation was complex, but in essence it would be a fixed fee contract, with a one-half-of-one-per cent incentive for good performance. The result was that North American would earn less than the usual 5.9 per cent of costs paid NASA contractors on average, and considerably less than the 7–7½- per cent profit paid by the Department of Defense for roughly similar work.[2]

Everything involving the Apollo contract was complicated, for a vast program was entailed. Some, at the time of the fire, said that NASA ought to scrap its contract with North American. Yet it is a measure of the difficulties of the space program that it would be totally impossible to do so— for no one else had the capability of continuing the program without months or years of delay. The bigger the programs get, the harder it is to move in any new direction. There is a growing tendency in the space business, as in defense, for government to be locked in with a handful of "sole sources."

Government has some protections, although they are not very swiftly applicable. First is the vast administrative machine within NASA, which moves ponderously but steadily to keep the level of the program high in accomplishment and control. Second, from the monetary standpoint, is the innate conservatism of the officers of the Bureau of the Budget, who tend to look with jaundiced eye on any new request not directly demanded by the President. Third is the process of the Renegotiation Board, an independent agency that surveys government contracts with business, after the fact.

The effectiveness of NASA's administrative machine is demonstrated by a development in NASA's Office of Industry Affairs in the spring and summer of 1969. For several years, as previously noted, the lead time between the acceptance of a program idea at all levels and the signing of a contract with a firm had crept ever upward until the average

[2] Interview with Martin Sacks, special assistant to Bernard Moritz.

in 1969 was 431 days. The situation was terrible and growing worse, so much so that it might wreck the program. With the agreement of all senior NASA officials, industry affairs assistant administrator George Vecchietti appointed a committee within NASA to investigate and make some recommendations. To help with the study Harvey M. Kennedy, Jr., a trained administrator, worked with Herbert L. Brewer, the former NASA deputy director of procurement; Brewer had gone to the Aerospace Industries Association, but came back for this purpose, it obviously being in the interest of the association to solve the problem. They studied sixty contracts, representing 30 per cent of those processed in two years and 19 per cent of all NASA dollars expended in that time.[3]

The committee found that NASA contracting had become a huge mess. Here is the procedure: When a project officer approves an idea, it goes to the program office whose workers prepare a "work statement" including specifications and drawings—the whole package that will be wanted. (As an example, the statement of work for the Space Station Program Definition [phase B] consisted of about three hundred typewritten pages.) This package then wends its way through the maze, starting at the space center where it was originated, and idling back to Washington headquarters. It goes to the director of procurement, to the program office, the legal office, the program support offices; then it is reviewed by the organization and management people, and finally it reaches the administrator, if it is a big enough program (five million dollars), or some official on the lower levels if it is smaller. It may sit around for months on various persons' desks—and the worst problem is that at every level

Interview with Harvey M. Kennedy, Jr.

the scores of people who see the papers seem to feel that they must comment on them and suggest improvements. This process requires meeting after meeting, which occupies week after week. Basically speaking, a plan to buy something from a contractor requires twenty-five steps within NASA, plus half as many concurrent steps; at one stage a dozen different people are looking over the plan at the same time, and until all twelve concur, the idea is stalled right there.

Brewer and Kennedy suggested that this mess be cleared up by reducing the flow to six steps and cutting many people off the mailing list—people who really did not need to see the material. It was a fine idea, but in the summer of 1969, two months after the study was finished, it was sitting on the desk of the head of the organization and management division of NASA—and he was on vacation. Probably the trimming would be accepted by everyone, and yet it was equally certain that in another five years the flow of paper work would have mounted again so that the process must be repeated. The trouble with bureaucracy is bureaucrats. There was no hope of recreating the informal atmosphere of the NACA days, when Ralph Cushman might be directed to buy something and go out and buy it. Buying had become procurement, and even Kennedy did not really hope to save more than perhaps a hundred days, which still meant that procurement would take almost a year even if his plan was followed.

The proof of the second control factor—the professional resistance of the Bureau of the Budget—was evidenced in its treatment of NASA requests every year, and especially in the pasting the agency budget took in 1960 when the Manned Space Flight program was slowed, until revived by President Kennedy the following year.

The third control, the Renegotiation Board, is an independent agency that moves slowly, but its wheels do grind. The Renegotiation Board was created to check on the profits of business firms which contract with the military services for weapons. In the interests of national security this defense contracting must remain secret, but because secrecy is also the dustbin for the concealment of mistakes and even peccadilloes, an agency such as the Renegotiation Board serves an important function.[4]

Each year, contractors who do business that amounts to more than a million dollars with the Department of Defense, the Maritime Administration, the Federal Maritime Board, the General Services Administration, the Atomic Energy Commission, the Federal Aviation Administration, and NASA, must file a report with the board. The board and its regional boards then decide which contracts they will look into. During 1968 the board investigated 4,354 contracts, cleared 3,527 of them at headquarters, and assigned 827, or 19 per cent, for further investigation. Some of these checks resulted in agreement by the companies to refund excess profits, some were cleared, and in some cases decisions were made not to proceed further. Of all, 238 cases were transferred to the headquarters of the board for more work.

In 1968 the board decided that various contractors had earned $23 million in excess profits during 1968, bringing the total excess profits since 1951 to nearly a billion dollars. In that total were two cases of considerable interest to the space business: those of McDonnell Douglas Corporation and North American Rockwell. The proceedings of the

[4] Interview with Howard W. Fensterstock, general counsel, Renegotiation Board.

board are kept secret in the interest of government-business amity, but these two cases both reached the tax court when the companies involved protested the levy of excess profits charges by the board.

In October 1965, McDonnell Douglas had filed its Renegotiation Board report as required, and the board looked it over. The report was originally cleared by the eastern regional board, but then in February 1966 the board itself decided to look into the case. A month later it informed McDonnell Douglas that it wanted a refund of $8 million in excess profits earned by the company on government business in 1965.

The company's renegotiable sales—those to the government agencies stipulated—came to $998,914,593 that year. What hurt was the board's reallocation of $18,755,000 of McDonnell's earnings on the Gemini spacecraft contract (NAS 9-170) from 1966 and other years to 1965.[5] The board also disallowed $2,564,438 which the company claimed as charitable contributions in 1965. The claim for refund by the board was made on the basis of the Gemini contract and the incentives granted the company by NASA, resulting in large fees. The board said the incentive fees were so large, and much too easily earned, because the target cost established by NASA and McDonnell for incentives "was overstated and unrealistic."[6]

McDonnell complained that the board failed to give due consideration to the risks the company ran in two contracts with the government, one to produce the Navy's Phantom II jet plane, and the other for Gemini. There had

[5] U.S. Tax Court case 1054 R, McDonnell Douglas Corporation vs Renegotiation Board, filings of plaintiff.
[6] *Ibid.*

been a lot of problems with the Phantom II, and the board cruelly claimed that they were McDonnell's fault.

The court case brought out the figures on Gemini and Mercury: for Gemini the costs were $647,906,000 and the company's earnings were $51,410,000, or 7.4 per cent. On Mercury, McDonnell had not fared so well: costs were $138,831,000 and earnings were $3,693,000, or only 2.6 per cent.

Obviously McDonnell's affairs had been looking up since the company's entry into the space business. In 1960 earnings had been $438,871,000—just about half what they were in 1965. As for returns: the board said McDonnell was getting a return on its capital of 24 to 27 per cent, a return on its book net worth of 50 to 60 per cent. Not bad.

McDonnell denied that it had made excessive profits on the Gemini program, and NASA officials agreed with the company. "They produced, they met the targets and surpassed them; they earned every cent," said George Vecchietti, NASA director of procurement.[7] The cost savings were the result of superior performance, said the company.

From the case, one also could get a glimpse of the nature of McDonnell's business. Not all its business was done with the United States government—only 98.4 per cent fell within the scope of the Renegotiation Board. Of that, 75 per cent consisted of the F-4 Phantom program for the Navy, air forces, and Marine Corps, and 21 per cent came from Gemini. That year, 1965, the company produced its one thousandth F-4, and 448 during the year. The Phantom represented the traditional business deal of a company with the government; the company's long experience in producing the plane and its assembly methods assured it of big

[7] George Vecchietti, interview with author.

profits. As for risk on Gemini, $28 million was assured the company regardless of performance. Where was the risk? What the government should have in these cases was the benefit of lower costs.

"The heavily expanded sales volume and increased profits, the reduced pricing risks, and the large amount of government financial assistance have been given due consideration," the board said. The year 1965 was the largest in McDonnell's twenty-six years of operation.

Other interesting questions coming out of the McDonnell case concerned government aid and the use to which McDonnell put its earnings. The company reinvested much money. It furnished 68.7 per cent of the plant and equipment for this government work, with the government furnishing 31.3 per cent. The ante in the space business was ever growing larger; what would happen to the companies that were not getting huge government contracts and not getting 31 per cent of the plant and equipment furnished by government?

The case of North American Rockwell (Docket No. 1063R) showed the same general pattern. North American Rockwell was also primarily a government-based business, with 98.2 per cent of its business in 1964 under government contract, 33 per cent of its sales in research and development and in manufacture of launch and space vehicles. The extent of North American Rockwell's business with the government was staggering:

6 Apollo spacecraft delivered, 4 flight tested
The S-II stage of the Saturn V launch vehicle
The F-1 rocket engine (1.5 million pounds thrust)
The J-2 rocket engine

33 H-1 engines for the first stages of Saturn I and IB launch
  vehicles
55 rocket engines for Atlas missiles
24 rocket engines for Thor missiles
3,000 engines for Redhead-Roadrunner, Shrike, Sparrow,
  and Sidewinder missiles
27 missions for the X-15
The XB-70 Mach 3 research aircraft
Guidance and control systems
Inertial navigation systems
System for nuclear auxiliary power (SNAP)

North American Rockwell pleaded that its profits were
not $9 million too high in 1964, as the board contended, be-
cause of the large risks involved to the company. When
there is basically only one customer, and that customer's
requirements shift frequently, the company has large risk—
it claimed. A true statement, but not altogether an accurate
picture of North American's problems. In 1964 North American Rockwell was so deeply involved in American defense
and space business, it is hard to see how it could substantially be hurt by any change in an order. By 1967 even
the Apollo fire could be surmounted without more than
mildly painful losses to the company. Doing business with
Army, Air Force, Navy, and NASA, the North American pattern was pretty well set. The problem was not so much the
company's risk in having only one customer, but the dangers to the government in depending upon ever bigger
and more powerful suppliers, and in competition lessening as
smaller companies were forced to merge, go out of business, or turn to other fields because the government contracts were becoming too large for any but the behemoths
to manage. Capability was the problem, and it was getting to

the point where a small firm might never achieve the capabilities required.

It was true, as North American Rockwell said, that the *production* contracts were subject to termination at the will of the government. The Air Force might discontinue a certain missile just after the company had absorbed all its developmental costs and was beginning to make real profits in the production lines. But in the space business this was not a problem. The company—and others with contracts—worked on a research and development basis. No matter how the company performed, it got paid.

In the Apollo program, North American Rockwell was engaged almost completely in research and development. Yet under the terms of the contract renegotiated *after* the fire in Apollo 7, the company earned $1,100,000 in incentive fees for performance between September 1, 1967, and December 31, 1968. It also earned $270,000 in incentive awards for performance in producing the second stage of the Saturn V launch vehicle in 1968. Research and development work for government might be binding in terms of restrictions, controls, and opportunities for long-term profits on a line of manufactures, but the companies engaged in large-scale research and development also had certain guarantees: the government furnished part of the equipment they used for testing and final preparation; the contracts they signed did not stipulate specific sums of money. In an ordinary business contract, the contractor guesses as best he can how much his costs will be, and then guarantees to bring in the product in stipulated numbers for that overall figure, which includes his theoretical costs and profits. But in a usual NASA prime contract, the bidder was given the job without *anyone* really knowing how much was going to be spent. Thus the contractor ran none of the usual business dangers. If the cost of development went sky-high, the government redid the contract or parts of it. The cost "overrun" became an expected adjunct to a contract.

In 1967 administrator Webb said NASA had some twenty thousand individual contracts. Actually, the prime contracts ($25 million and over) in the spring of 1969 numbered fifty-two—which did not mean, however, that there were fifty-two prime contractors. North American Rockwell, in its various divisions, led all the rest with eight prime contracts totaling more than five and three-quarter *billions* of dollars.[8]

Second in *number* of contracts held was Bendix Corporation, with four contracts totaling $281 million. Third came a group of five companies, each holding three contracts: Grumman, $2 billion; Boeing, $1,400 million; General Electric, $898 million; International Business Machines, $500 million; TRW, $121 million. Fourth was a group of five companies, each holding two contracts: McDonnell Douglas, $1,100 million; Aerojet General, $570 million; Sperry Rand, $80 million; Lockheed, $70 million; RCA, $58 million. Finally came sixteen companies with single contracts, ranging from Chrysler's $490 million and General Motors' $370 million to Federal Electric's $31 million and ILC Industries' $27 million.

The big space business, then, rested with only twenty-eight different firms, and of this the billion-dollar contracts were in the hands of only five firms, with North American having more than twice as much space business as its nearest competitor, Grumman.

[8] The source for this and following figures is *NASA Procurement Program Policies and Trends Handbook,* fiscal year 1969.

The picture did change from time to time within the field. McDonnell in 1969 was just barely in the billion-dollar class, with Mercury and Gemini completed, but it might be back up there at any time because the government had a very high regard for McDonnell Douglas's "experience and capability." Martin Marietta, which was way down on the list with a single $33 million contract, had surged back to secure the Viking space probe vehicle contract, which might eventually put Martin into the billion-dollar class, depending on how it went and government policies of the future.

Granting all that volatility in the space business, still it was apparent that the business was becoming frighteningly self-limiting, by virtue of its very business. It was conceivable, of course, that General Motors or Chrysler could step out and snatch a big chunk of the space business—or was it? Would even such big companies be willing to expend the hundreds of millions of dollars to establish the plant facilities and "capability" to compete for the big contracts in the space business? The indications were that the trend was the other way. The names suggest it: McDonnell-Douglas, North American-Rockwell, Hiller-Fairchild-Republic. Would it soon be Boeing-Grumman, Bendix-Hughes, United-Lockheed? That is the history of the automobile business, the great precursor to space business in the industrial history of America. The grave difference, from the standpoint of the national weal, is that the automobile companies have millions of customers, while the space companies have basically one customer. If one considers that most of these big space companies are also the big defense contractors for missiles and air devices and systems, the problem is even more serious, so serious that the RAND Corporation in 1969 established a special study group to examine the situation, performance, and possible control of these contractors.[9]

The RAND study would be made for the Air Force and would not be binding on anyone, but the fact that the Department of Defense was showing so much concern was of more than passing interest.

This problem of bigness was caused by the nature of the space industry, so closely allied to defense with its necessary secrecy, and the nature of American society. Americans have had an open society and relish the idea of keeping it that way, even though the opening is not as large as it was a half-century ago. One very serious difficulty, encountered time and again in making this study, is the reluctance of space businessmen to talk about their business, and in particular about the manner in which they have secured space contracts. One representative of Martin Marietta was finally quite frank about the secrecy: "We are not inclined to talk about our business outside," he said. He gave as reasons the company's concern about quotation out of context, worry about public discussions of the "military industrial complex," and the general reluctance of competitive industrialists to talk about their affairs.[10] The exceptions to this reluctance were, unsurprisingly, the American Telephone and Telegraph Company (whose place in the space business was thoroughly prescribed by the Kennedy Administration in the Bellcomm contract), and, surprisingly, North American, which provided many facts and figures, although none that would assist any competitors. But basically, he who seeks information about the business workings of the space in-

9 William Putnam, late of NASA, in 1969 of RAND Corporation in interview with author.
10 William McBride of Martin Marietta, to author, summer 1969.

dustry goes to NASA, where discussion of specific contracts is very guarded (NASA's deep concern for its relations with the contractors); and to the various hearings of the committees on Capitol Hill which have made exhaustive examinations of aspects of the space business from time to time.

If Congress had total access to all information about the space business, that might be enough for public protection. In his day, administrator Webb offered several times in hearings to give information in executive session that he did not wish to give in public. The committees were generally reluctant to take that responsibility, and preferred to dig away in public hearing. Because of the success of the Apollo project and the newness of the Nixon Administration's administrator Thomas O. Paine in the job, the NASA budget authorization hearings in the spring of 1969 were mild. Even Senator Margaret Chase Smith, who has often been a searching critic of the space program, contented herself with noting improvements in communications between administrator Webb and Congress, and abjuring Paine to keep a greater eye on economy in the future.[11]

Among the other business problems that dogged the space agency in 1969 was the unsolved problem of the astronauts and their personal business dealings. When the first seven astronauts were picked in 1959, they were allowed—even encouraged—to make a joint venture of their personal adventures in the space program. NASA wanted to avoid trouble, and its legal department encouraged the astronauts in the $500,000 contract they signed with *Life* magazine for the rights to use their personal narratives.

The success of this venture led the astronauts into

[11] Hearings Before Committee on Aeronautical and Space Sciences, United States Senate, 91st Congress, NASA authorization for fiscal year 1970, p. 10.

others further afield, including a plunge into the real estate market with the operation of a motel on the strip at Cocoa Beach. NASA had to step in, finally, and cause the astronauts to divest themselves of such flagrant abuses of their preferred positions. It was one thing to sell their personal narratives, and another to use the taxpayers' investment in them to compete with legitimate, outside business.

In the spring of 1969 *The New York Times* estimated that the then fifty-five astronauts (salaries $15,000–$27,000) and the eight widows of astronauts who shared equally in the joint program would receive an additional $16,000 each during the year as a result of the sale and syndication of the personal accounts of the astronauts who made the moon. Thus, although three men would participate in the lunar landings, all the astronauts and widows would participate in the cash.[12]

This development represents an interesting change in the concept, function, and rights of "heroes" in America. In the past the Lindberghs and the Admiral Byrds supported themselves and their ventures by writing about them and contracting for the sale of their writings. But they were not engaged in government ventures, as were the astronauts. Lindbergh, Byrd, and the other heroes paid for their adventures out of their own pockets for the most part. To be sure, an Admiral Halsey, or a General Eisenhower, could earn a great deal of money with the various rights to his life story, but that was a one-shot proposition. The astronaut venture represents the combined efforts of tens of thousands of people to put a man on the moon. Some cynics have suggested that the astronauts' earnings in private affairs from their work ought to go back into the public treasury.

[12] *The New York Times*, June 22, 1969.

The business affairs of the astronauts are a matter of more interest than even their publishing success would indicate. At least ten of them are members of the boards of directors or consultants to companies which produce various space throw-offs: toys, books, postcards, and other devices glorifying these astronauts are sold freely in the open market; they are even sold at the Kennedy Space Center. Is there an ethical problem in this capitalization of community effort? Is there any difference between astronauts becoming bank directors or running for Congress, and astronauts lending their names to a toy manufacturer?

These are interesting questions because it is apparent in 1971 that in the future America the frontiers are going to be in space and under the sea—both areas in which only government will have the resources to back the exploration programs. The day of the individual hero is pretty well done, we know, even if Hollywood and the novelists had not forced this information into us in massive draughts of nonhero and antihero medicines. But we still operate, in the secret recesses of our living rooms, with the heroic attitude, and there is created an anomaly for the future to consider.

One point about the astronauts' business affairs was made by Paul P. Haney, former NASA public affairs officer at the Manned Spacecraft Center at Houston:

"The best thing about the contract" (with *Life*), he said, "from the astronauts' point of view is that it gives them leverage against NASA." Haney said that the astronauts did not like being plagued by interviewers from the press, and that when NASA public affairs people suggested interviews, they might decline by citing the contract with *Life*.[13] Is this, then, to be the point of such business deal-

13 *Ibid.*

ings, to give the appointed heroes "leverage" against government?

In the spring and summer of 1969, several of the scientist-astronauts and others connected with the scientific program of NASA resigned in annoyance with the continued emphasis on engineering and exploration rather than science. That news was a welcome diversion from the all-too-usual reports of the astronauts being more concerned with their business affairs than with the space program.

NASA became enough concerned with the outside activities of the astronauts to draw up a sixty-page document called "Standard of Conduct for NASA Employees." The point of the booklet, according to its author (Paul Dembling of the NASA general counsel's office), is to prevent conduct that will discredit the agency. Yet stock market investment, directorships in various corporations, associations with toymakers, metals, communications, life insurance, systems, and other companies all carry the potential threat of a public outcry. Just as certainly as there will be other accidents in the space program, one day some company will make injudicious use of its astronaut's name and position, and then the fat will be in the fire. The first seven astronauts very nearly came under Congressional investigation when a Houston builder offered them free houses as a promotion for his business. NASA did not allow the astronauts to accept the houses, and by this margin the Congressional investigation of their business activities was avoided. Perhaps it ought not to have been. Congress does not usually investigate or legislate in the abstract; it will probably take a full-scale scandal to secure the kind of change in relationship between the new class of federally subsidized, federally employed explorers and the government that is in the long-range public interest. The astronauts have done nothing reprehensible enough to occasion such an investigation, but as they grow in number and the business community encourages them to increase their activities, it is almost bound to come.

Some aspects of the space business are worrisome in a time when technological change is outracing American society's ability to deal with it; other developments simply are cause for joy, such as the little-trumpeted fact that nearly three thousand new ideas have been generated in the space business that are applicable elsewhere. Some of the most promising and spectacular are in the field of medicine, such as the telemetry unit produced by a small firm to monitor the electrocardiograms of the astronauts while they performed various duties. Hospitals have taken up the idea with one modification, for use in intensive-care sections.

Other sensors designed for the astronauts have also found their way into medical use: an automatic alarm that watches over hospital patients with breathing problems; a computer that helps clarify medical X rays; a sensor that measures muscle tremors, specifically useful in Parkinson's disease; a meter that measures the elasticity of bones in the aged. In other fields there are a TV camera the size of a cigarette package that can monitor industrial processes; an electromagnetic hammer that smoothes weld seams without weakening them; bearings coated with a ceramic-bonded dry lubricant for use at high temperatures. There are so many uses in industry for computers that a special computer-use center has been established. According to a 1969 NASA release, citing developments:

> *A computer program designed to optimize a group of design parameters has been requested by over three-thousand*

different companies throughout the U.S. At the Bonneville power dam, for example, engineers used it to optimize the design of control circuitry, while General Foods applied it to optimize the variables in food preparation and produce consistent foods. . . .[14]

In the new uses to which scientific and engineering developments are being put in industry, the space business has contributed a very great deal to American life quite inside the atmosphere.

So many and far-reaching were the developments that NASA established a special Technology Utilization Program, to make available to all American business the developments within the space business that are applicable elsewhere. In 1970 five million dollars was budgeted for this purpose, half of it simply for dissemination of information. NASA had another little bureaucracy on its hands, but a most useful one to business. It appointed technology utilization officers to work with business, and issued a series of publications called *Tech Aids* which describe the new technologies. It set up regional dissemination centers which had computerized use of seven hundred thousand reports, a library growing in 1969 at the rate of six thousand reports a month. In a decade the library would double, but perhaps half the information would be obsolete by that time. So intricate was the system already that NASA employed the Denver Research Institute under contract to study experimental dissemination techniques in order to get word of new processes out to business more quickly.

Among the developments, Hayes International Corporation built for Marshall Space Flight Center a lightweight portable router to machine heavy subassemblies in place.

[14] Summary Descriptive Information on a Random Selection of Transfer Examples, NASA Technology Utilization Division, March 1969.

This was converted by Newport News Shipbuilding and Dry Dock Company to the shipping business. McDonnell Douglas built a portable air cleaner for the Manned Spacecraft Center and has marketed it for public use. Many applications and inventions have come from the space laboratories themselves. Ames Research Center developed miniature FM transmitters for broadcasting biomedical data from space capsules, and these are in use in industrial plants to check machinery.

The space business was shooting off many little saplings, from which great businesses might grow. The government was accepting a new responsibility in the 1960's; with the expenditure of $15 billion a year in research and development (one-quarter of it by NASA), government was trying to disseminate the information.[15] NASA had a major role, this agency that had grown to employ thirty-two thousand people at twenty locations, and involve the services of an estimated four hundred thousand people serving the twenty thousand contractors.

One of the big problems in preserving the technology developed in the space business is one that has dogged industry before now: American business has no sense of history. NASA found fairly early in the game that the technology developed in designing certain bits of equipment was forgotten in the rush of events. Nobody wrote it down, or if they did it was dropped into the wastebasket somewhere along the line. Similarly, a company might make an expensive study of some cosmic rarity, but if the study failed for some reason, the company was likely to file and forget—and not once, but many times, the same study might

[15] Statement by Richard Lesher, assistant administrator, NASA, for Technology Utilization.

be proposed again. If, as happened so often in the space program, the people who had engineered the first study were gone to other employment, then the study might be repeated, uselessly and wastefully.

NASA brought a certain order from this industrial chaos by hiring and stationing technology utilization officers in major NASA field offices to review research and development. This means reading and reading and reading plenty. In one six-month period one center screened sixty-three thousand abstracts for Ball Brothers Company of Muncie, Indiana, getting out 153 that would be useful to the company.[16]

The order came when NASA insisted that NASA contractors working on government research and development programs disclose their inventions, discoveries, and improved techniques, and that the inventions become the property of NASA. But in practice, NASA can and does waive the rights to the invention from time to time, with the reservation that the government can use the invention. The question of public policy raised here is an interesting one that may some day become vital. If NASA pays the freight, should not the inventions belong to the taxpayers? But if industry is constantly giving away its inventions, what will become of its competitive position?

Those inventions that interest NASA are patented by the agency and made available to American business, royalty-free. But in the future, as the space business continues to expand its offshots, there will be a new bureaucracy in the investigation and control of patents from government-sponsored research. For NASA policy provides that if a NASA-owned invention has not been developed into com-

[16] Lesher statement, April 28, 1969.

mercial form within two years after a patent is issued, NASA will make the invention available *exclusively* to one company to stimulate interest in using the invention commercially.

Whatever the benefits to the public from this very close intermingling of government and business, it is apparent that NASA is on the brink of transcending the space business and becoming involved in general business affairs, if only through its patent applications program. The power to grant patents for exclusive development is a very great power, and can mean the creation of fortunes in American business; there is question as to whether NASA ought to have this power at all.

There are many unresolved questions about the space business as it goes into its second decade in the United States, questions which in their extension affect the way of business, the way of government, and the way of life of the American people. The RAND study of defense contractors, their competence and performance, comes at a very important time, and none too soon. But the RAND study cannot be expected to deal with the overall policies of government-business relationships. This area is one with which Congress ought to concern itself, if for no other reason than that the development of government-business relationships as it is occurring now threatens to further erode the practical power of Congress to deal with the biggest industries in the country. The "military-industrial complex" may not be the bogeyman it has been painted; but the "government-industrial complex" threatens to spread wider every year, constantly eroding the ability of small firms to compete and that of the public to protect individual liberty.

In 1970 President Nixon cut the space budget very severely, showing at least that space was not the runaway program that defense had been since 1945, that the government was still in control of the activities, and that politicians were still in control of policy. Administrator Paine resigned shortly thereafter. In 1970 the space companies also indicated the growing difficulty private enterprise was having in gearing up for the efforts that would be necessary for any new space projects. And the two most successful firms, McDonnell-Douglas and North American Rockwell, were working together to try to snag big new hardware contracts, as were less successful competitors of the past. By mid-year Boeing was in trouble economically, too.

By the end of the year most of American business was in trouble for different reasons. Yet the aerospace business continued to suffer from its special problem in addition to all the other problems. For an example, take the case of an electronics engineer whom I shall call B. He was employed by a Cambridge, Massachusetts, engineering firm until the firm lost its aerospace contract because of the slowdown at NASA, and then, shortly, B lost his job. So many other specialists in his field lost their jobs almost simultaneously that soon the fifty-six-year-old B lost hope and decided to go into business for himself as a handyman and "fix-it" man rather than compete for jobs that seemed to be nonexistent. Even granting that the supply of skilled artisans in 1971 in America was not high, was it economically or socially sound to force a highly trained professional man to this work?

The further tragedy of B lies in the "information explosion" of the 1970's, whereby B will find himself out of touch with his field because of a few months of inactivity. He will be so far behind in techniques that his employability will undoubtedly suffer. B might be able to catch up easily enough, but to convince an employer of it would be something else again. He might be completely unemployable in his specialty, too.

All the more emphasis is cast here on the wastefulness of the space program in human as well as economic terms—the way it is managed in America in the 1970's. Americans may think we have too many Ph.D.'s, engineers, students, and scientists, as seems to be the trend. But the state of the national progress in terms of the many national challenges, to say nothing of world challenges, belies the concept of overabundance. Can it be true that the capitalist system will be unable to meet the challenges of the last quarter of the twentieth century?

Aerospace is typical of our most highly specialized industries and activities in one way: in human terms there is far too much waste of talent in the competitive manner in which we have operated in the past. The Von Kormanns and the Von Brauns did not do their best work in their early years, and might not ever have done their best work at all had they moved from one job and one project to another constantly. Needless to say, the waste of training a man, then shunting him aside for a younger man when the training has come to fruition, seems obviously self-defeating. Experience and continuity used to be valued in American industry and science, but continuity and experience cannot be retained in a volatile economic situation where the gold ring goes only to one firm and the employees of its competitor face large question marks at best.

Speaking economically, the space program is equally wasteful, with billions of dollars in profits going out of the taxpayers' pockets and into the hands of the space dealers. It had always been the American way to put profits into weaponry; and the defense-contracting industry, which is very similar to the space business in terms of companies competing, had grown to become very nearly an arm of government, so closely were the contractors allied with defense matters. The question this raises is, why not an arm of government, or why not very strict government controls of such industries? It would seem that the time had come to strip away the glamour and bring the space dealers, along with the weapons dealers, under public control.

Bibliography

Specific references are noted in the chapter notes, but the following volumes were of particular value in the general preparation of this work.

COOKE, DAVID C., Editor, *The Aircraft Annual, 1945*, New York, Robert McBride and Co., 1945.

EMME, EUGENE M., Editor, *The History of Rocket Technology*, Detroit, Wayne State University Press, 1964.

HAGGERTY, JAMES J., and SMITH, WARREN REILAND, *The U.S. Air Force: A Pictorial History*, New York, Books Inc., 1966.

KILLEN, JOHN, *A History of the Luftwaffe*, Garden City, N.Y., Doubleday, 1968.

LEHMAN, MILTON, *This High Man, the Life of Robert Goddard*, New York, Farrar Straus and Co., 1963.

LEY, WILLY, *Rockets, Missiles and Men in Space*, New York, Viking, 1968.

MODLEY, RUDOLF, Editor, *Aviation Facts and Figures, 1945*, New York, McGraw, 1945.

NAYLER, J. L., *Aviation, Its Technical Development*, Philadelphia, Dufour Editions, 1965.

ROSHOLT, ROBERT L., *An Administrative History of NASA, 1958–1963*, prepared under the auspices of the NASA historical staff, Washington, NASA, 1966.

SWENSON, LOYD S., JR.; GRIMWOOD, JAMES M.; and ALEXANDER, CHARLES C., *This New Ocean, A History of Project Mercury*, Washington, The NASA Historical Series, NASA, 1966.

VON BRAUN, WERNHER, and ORDWAY, FREDERICK I., III, *History of Rocketry and Space Travel*, New York, T. Y. Crowell, 1966.

VON KARMAN, THEODORE, and EDSON, LEE, *The Wind and Beyond*, Boston, Little Brown, 1967.

Index